What's Really Eating You?

*Overcome the Triggers
of Comfort Eating*

Renée Jones

Ainsley&Allen
PUBLISHING

Ainsley & Allen Publishing LLC
2035 Sunset Lake Road
Newark, DE 19702
www.ainsleyallenpublishing.com

ISBN-13: 978-0-9975855-4-4
ISBN-10: 997585544

"Face your stuff—don't stuff your face! Renée Jones puts a complex truth in a few simple words. Sensitively guiding us to face our own limiting (eating) behaviour, she opens doors for personal growth and taking (back) our responsibility for a healthy lifestyle. In an easy-to-read and down-to-earth way, she writes about being aware of our thoughts, attitude and therefore behaviour related to eating and beyond. I have been waiting for this book for a long time. Thank you for writing it." – *Melanie König, Königstraining Training and Coaching, Germany*

"Renée Jones shares her personal journey with eating, over-eating, and emotional eating with candid honesty. That would be interesting in itself, and yet it is much more than that because the lessons she learnt on the way are applicable to so many other people. By sharing her practical no nonsense help, advice, tips, and insights, she gives others the permission to be themselves, for better or worse, exactly as any excellent coach should. In turn people are free to choose differently, change, and free themselves of their past patterns of behaviour—as well as starting to enjoy food and eating again!" –*Elizabeth Mansfield, Trainer, coach and therapist, Help-me-lose-weight-now.com, England*

"After a lifetime of fighting weight issues, I'm ready to deal with the truth. It's time for gut-level honesty, and Renée Jones provides practical applications to long-term problems. Now that I understand my triggers, I can stop fearing the scale. When I face what's eating me, I'm able to tackle those things I don't want to admit. No more anxiety...thanks, Renée." – *Shari Barnes, University instructor and retired Director of Employee Relations*

"Renée Jones changes the way we think of weight loss. Say 'goodbye' to dieting and 'hello' to a healthy life!" – *Bruce Prindle, D. Min.*

"Like most of us, the hits and dings Renée Jones has taken have made her stronger and very perceptive to others' pain. She brings all of that to her sessions with her clients and this book, asking the best questions, helping you come to your 'ah-ha' moment." – *Marsha R. West, retired principal, school board member, and theatre arts teacher. Author of* Vermont Escape, Truth Be Told, Second Act, Act of Trust, *and* The Theatre.

"Smart and genuine! Renée is generous with sharing 'her stuff' so the reader gets an inside, up close view of you while getting a better view of themselves. She took an everyday struggle and provided a clear, concise road map to success." – *Cindy Smith-Adkins, Director of Managed Care*

Dedication

I'm truly grateful for the many, many people who have taught, influenced, and encouraged me, read, re-read, read again, and proofread the material, and listened to my joys and frustrations as a growing writer. Your patience, wisdom, and kindness continue to propel me toward this dream and my mission.

So very grateful I stumbled into the path of Elizabeth Mansfield, who helped me break my own yo-yo and resolve my triggers along with a lorry-load of other things. God used you to help me back to myself and my path. Genuinely, thank you.

To Jack Canfield, Steve Harrison, Trish Troilo, Martha Bullen, Deb Englander, Geoffrey Berwind, Bill Harrison, and Dave Holland for very practical guidance and assistance on said path.

To J. Suzanne Frank, Barbara Miercort, and the Writer's Path at SMU along with Becki, Kirsten, Betty, Margaret, Christine, and Amy for teaching, reading, and encouraging for so very many years.

To Lewis Chambers at Bethel Agency who took me on and believed in me.

To my dear Auntie Hugh Delle, the grammar guru, for answering endless questions so I might make my English teacher mother proud and spare editor Heidi Graeul excess work.

To Mrs. Woods, from 6th grade, who helped me identify and encourage writing as an option.

To friends, family, and colleagues who read, encouraged, and called me to my best: Kathy, Bruce, Melanie, Shari, Marsha, Cindy, Jane, Meredith, Melani, Jane and David, Claire and Ken, Diane, Bill, Caroline, and Tricia.

To my precious Nan, thanks for the loving encouragement and practical wisdom.

Most, to the ever wonderful, wise, patient, and irreplaceable Michael —thank you for this adventure, love. It wouldn't be without you.

Table of Contents

Introduction

I spent 40 years on a perpetual diet, losing and gaining hundreds of pounds. Since my first diet started when I was 10, and I came from a family of fairly large women, I learned every diet going—I also learned every cheat. And I learned that once the diet was abandoned or we reached a magic number, we returned to how we'd always eaten, finally free to eat what and how much we wanted again, and the cycle continued.

Just before my 50th birthday, I finally lost that "last 20 pounds" yet again, but something was different this time. I hadn't found the latest version of low-fat/-carb/-calorie or magic potion that makes the weight fall right off you. I'd dealt with my "stuff" that triggered comfort eating, which saved a surprising number of calories. I made new choices about foods, I created new habits, and I woke up from the stupor of the all-you-can-eat buffet.

It wasn't easy, but it did turn out to be a fairly simple process in the end. Mind, when I was staring down the chocolate chips in the pantry one day, it didn't feel so simple, but it worked as I learned how to make different choices.

Over three years later, I lost another five pounds, and today I'm well within the recommended weight range for my height and build. It still fluctuates week to week, as is normal, but my consistent choices maintain my weight.

Can I eat anything I want every day? No. I never could—and that's the point. Just as we make good choices for our financial budget, work schedule, and family needs that do not entail getting everything we want, we can make good choices for our nutritional budget that achieve our long-term goals. The triggers of comfort eating can be disarmed and overcome.

This material offers a guide to facing our stuff and making different choices. Your experiences will be different, and I hope you find the parallels that can free you from emotional, stress, and comfort eating.

Each chapter begins with a **Quick-Start Guide**, including ideas that helped me and my clients along the way, and ends with **Shifting Gears**, ideas for applying the lessons from the chapters. **For Your Consideration** lists questions from the chapter to assist in your process.

I hope this becomes a useful tool in helping you overcome your triggers of comfort eating and reaching your goals. For a free gift, visit FreeGift.PackYourOwnBag.com.

"There is nothing new under the sun." Ecclesiastes 1:9

CHAPTER ONE

Forty Years on a Diet

Quick Start Guide: Things That Work

Before you begin a new plan, take a three-day personal food holiday—eat anything and everything you could possibly want. Don't limit yourself, and do not go to guilt or shame. This is an exercise for you to simply enjoy the foods you love and have craved. It will do no good if you don't just cut loose and enjoy your favorites, so go for it.

Yes, you will probably gain a little, but at this point, that's okay. Just let it be.

There is one rule: Take the time to enjoy every bite or sip you take. Don't wolf down the food or chug-a-lug the beverage. Chew it thoroughly, and squeeze every bit of flavor from the morsel. If it's a beverage, hold it in your mouth and allow all the flavor facets to roll over your taste buds. Take time to savor every bite or sip.

If you stop savoring, stop putting it in your mouth. You can have ANYTHING you want, but you must enjoy it. You have permission. In fact, you have a mandate.

All diets—low fat, low carb, high protein, keto, banana and grapefruit, Sensible Eating, the French Paradox, The Ice Cream Diet, DASH, zones, types, points, metabolic analysis, alkaline, liquid, fasting, Fat Bombs, Sirtfood, to the self-titled plans—have a secret. They all work for someone, at least for a while, even if not all diets work for everyone all the time. Even the nutzo diets we know, love, and loathe do work at least to some degree while we follow them.

Many of them were my constant companions as I sought THE ONE that would "make the weight just fall off" as I spent 40 years gaining and losing and gaining and losing, and yes, gaining and losing over and over again. It's maddening, and yet there is no easy way around it until we find the way to maintain the loss we work so hard to achieve. Lasting weight management is finding the combination of intake, exercise, and consistent choices we can live with emotionally, mentally, spiritually, and physically. Some people do better with fewer carbohydrates, others with a balance of carbohydrates, protein, and fats. We're all different, and sometimes our mental and emotional sides are at odds with our physical, and our spiritual sides may be pounding on everything else. We may not be in the right frame of mind to focus on nutrition. If we're not mentally ready—or if we're completely desperate to fit in that outfit by Saturday—it's harder to get lasting results.

There truly is nothing new under the sun. The latest and greatest sounding "diet" that worked for Auntie Delle's best friend would be great if my lifestyle, flavor preferences, body composition, and metabolism were the same. However, since she's five-feet eight-inches tall, lean of build, extremely active, and doesn't even like sweet things, and I'm only five-foot-three, so solid of build that my brother's high school friends referred to me as a "linebacker," more couch potato in nature, and sugar is like crack to me, what are the chances?

That magic diet, detox, flush, or pill that promises a 10-pound weight loss in a week is seldom quite so magic in the end. We know that, and yet… the idea still makes our hearts quicken, doesn't it? The promises, the hope, the freedom from having to work at it are so alluring, but alas usually such bull. Even surgical intervention hasn't cured the ailment consistently. Following a bypass, band, sleeve, or other version, many people lose weight rapidly. For some, it works, and they've learned how to manage their intake to maintain their goal weight. However, many of my clients have come to me after they've regained their weight within five years. They didn't maintain the healthy choices, slowly returned to their previous eating habits, and are again looking for a way to lose the weight.

If you want to get a group of women going in conversation, just throw in the weight loss card. Everyone has an idea, something that worked, or the latest magic diet. They work for a time... until we revert to our old ways or divert from the basic plan. I so wish I could deliver that promised magic pill. *No work, just take this, and the weight will fall off you. No muss, no fuss, no pain, and no regaining the weight when you finish the (automatic reorder of the) 90-day supply.* It would be fantastic to free generations from the challenge, frustration, shame, guilt, and near torture that weight management has become. It would be a gift to humanity, wouldn't it?

In many ways, we've made it more complicated and torturous. We eat more than our bodies need so our waistlines expand, and we torture ourselves by heaping shame and guilt along with the stress we're feeling from other areas. We justify (pick your poison) chocolate/salty snacks/bread/that cheap white cake with butter cream frosting and sprinkles as the most efficient way to relieve that stress in this moment. We don't have time to sort it out. Just give me the cake! Then later we scold and shame ourselves when our waists exceed our waistbands.

When we again want to reduce, we feel it as deprivation and punishment. We are separated from the cool kids, the group who can eat whatever, and, again, we torture ourselves with thinking... what? What is it we are thinking that isn't helping us nor supporting our goals?

Those specific thoughts not only make "dieting" harder, they make it less effective, and we are beat up in the process. The fact that we've tried it before to varying degrees of success doesn't help either. When I tried X, it didn't work for me. Or that one worked until Y. Managing our weight is as much mental and emotional as physical.

The secret to maintenance is finding the lifestyle choices we can live with. There is no magic to any diet, but there is a combination of foods, portions, and exercise that fits your particular needs. Finding that combination is your unique challenge to accept or reject. You live with the results either way, but you still have that choice. It likely won't be instantaneous. We didn't get into our weight issues overnight, and we cannot dismantle all of our coping mechanisms that quickly, but we can disarm those triggers to effect lasting change.

I went on my first diet was when I was 10. In the 1970s, many schools in Texas had yet to add air conditioning to elementary school buildings, and apparently we didn't really think about any version of lunch box refrigeration, so when I opened my lunch box, the scent of some kind of fish wafted up before I saw it in all its pale, filleted lack of glory. My skinny little friends were eating things that looked so good, and I had a tasteless, salt-free, and colorless lunch of fish with a side of iceberg lettuce and celery salad. White and pale green. Maybe there was a stray carrot for some color, but nutritional favors like baby lettuces spring mix hadn't yet arrived at our local A&P.

One would think that kind of gustatory ostracism would spur one to knuckle down, get it done, and learn how to eat best for my body type to avoid that situation ever again. I'd love to meet the person who declared victory after one diet and could maintain the loss indefinitely. How did they do that? Perhaps they had the lightning bolt moment and either learned how to budget foods and exercise or eliminated food from their list of coping mechanisms, applying their knowledge more effectively. It obviously took me quite a bit more practice.

All the pictures from my childhood are of a thin little red-haired girl. My mother said I ate like a bird—a little bit all day long, never too much at one time, stopping for a bite of something now and again. I enjoyed my food but didn't eat too much for my needs. I was satisfied and stopped eating without any emotional attachment or concern about cleaning my plate. Even in the 1960s, we had plastic wrap. It would still be in the refrigerator if and when I was ready for the next top-up. Note that my plate still had to be clean before the end of day, of course, but my mother apparently grew weary of the drama of forcing me to complete my meals at one sitting. Would that subsequent babysitters had had such wisdom and patience.

Then came school. Kindergarten was transitional, and by the time I hit first grade, we all wondered what happened to that thin little redhead. She blossomed into a 6X, the size for chunkier girls, and I knew immediately that it was an accepted curse of life. Looking at the women in my extended family, I was resigned to acknowledging we weren't meant to be thin. If you were, you were a bit of a traitor, and corporate wisdom said that one day no one could fight it anymore, and you'd fall back in line as you grew up and out. Age and weight were intertwined.

Grade school meant fitting into new schedules of sitting in a classroom for hours rather than running about, and new rules about cleaning one's plate in the designated 20-minute school lunch period, eating what you're given, and doing as you're told. All are well-intentioned teachings that impart good lessons about discipline, responsibility, and respect geared for the life stage. The issue is that we get stuck there.

How many times have you cleaned your plate because that's what you were taught rather than because you were hungry or actually wanted it?

Yes, and I have. Even today, if I don't have the option of a takeaway container at a restaurant, I might have to talk to myself quite adamantly about the ultimate merits of leaving food on my plate. Waisting it vs. Wasting it. Deeply imbedded lessons take significant intention and attention.

Just as we grew out of walking everywhere in a line with our eyes forward, mouths shut, and hands to ourselves, we can grow into new self-chosen rules about that clean plate and other remains of childhood and family of origin issues. We easily shed other rules and habits that no longer fit our lives. If we come in from an evening and go to bed by nine p.m., it's because we want to rather than because of a curfew. We love the freedom of no longer having to have a licensed driver in the passenger seat next to us when we drive. We do complex study of a chosen subject because we find it fascinating rather than because we have to perform for an exam. Yet habits of how we eat, when, where, what, how much, and why do tend to get stuck.

It should be common sense, shouldn't it?

If it were, we would all be doing it by now.

My precious grandmother shimmied into her girdle every day. No matter whether she was in jeans working on the ranch or getting gussied up to go to town, she put on that girdle to hold in her curves. Bless her!

Not that her compression garments were easy to slip into. To do the job, it had to be a tight fit, and she had to pull and tug through quite a workout—a bit like trying to get into skinny jeans or buttoning the waist of a pair of jeans that are really a size or two too small, but if you just hold your breath and suck in everything… it Just. Might. Button.

What I found interesting is that she would make that effort every day. Every day. She would handle the breathing constriction all day. She'd suffer the discomfort of restricted movement all day. She'd drive 25 miles to the nearest town to buy new ones when they no longer held adequately. She focused a lot of effort and attention on obtaining and maintaining this method of holding in her stomach and hips.

Foundation garments, also known as shape wear, control-top, slimming panels, corsets, body briefers, compression garments, and the "girdle," have assisted women and men for centuries to counter the results of lapses in control, judgment, or choices. It covers a multitude of sins, and it's a whole lot easier than making different choices about food, whether that was quantity, quality, or how we combine fats, proteins, and carbohydrates. It's also easier than dealing with the stress, sadness, memories, and frustration that trigger our need for comfort. Food is the easy and quick means of comfort—not to mention part of our expression of happiness, joy, and many other emotions. Food is both celebration and a cure for what ails you.

Or perhaps you defied the family pattern. The family you spend the most time with is lean and slim, and you took your primary genes from the other side. All the weight just sort of ganged up on your hips when most of your relatives are skinny. And maybe they work at it, but maybe they don't, and that feels like the cruel joke of genetic chance. The difference in freedom of choice is frustrating and uncomfortable, and perhaps it also drives you to comfort yourself with food, again a cure for what ails you.

Say hello to emotional eating.

Not that it doesn't work. A pint of ice cream straight from the carton does something positive in the moment to soothe, calm, and somehow meet a need that we can't quite name. The empty carton is also a handy place to cram that pile of tear-stained tissues when you've regained your balance. It does work, and then the wrap-around guilt jumps up to bite us with the familiar refrain of negative self-talk.

Fill in the blank: with what words do you beat yourself? We know them well, don't we? We've used them enough. Does it help? Ever?

A simple web search will produce many different types of diets as well as conflicting information about why they work or don't. Doctors do not even agree on the mechanism of weight gain or loss because nutritional science is so incredibly complex. Everyone is unique—in chemistry, emotions, desire for change, accountability needs, specific food issues or triggers, and preferences.

It surprises my clients, but I never give a specific diet. They already likely know many diets—some they like, some they don't. My suggestion is that they pick one and follow it or create one that works for them. "The Diet" itself is not the magic bullet. The key is finding the nutrition plan that works for the individual—palatable, efficient, satiating, and fits the lifestyle they choose. That takes care of what to eat, when to eat, portion sizes, and all of those issues. It's a big piece, but it's only one piece.

Exercise is helpful, and there are a gazillion programs available on that as well. My recommendation for exercise is this: Get some. Then exercise other aspects of choice, emotion, and guidance. For the physical, a walk is good, some weight bearing exercise tones and builds muscle, and stretching is helpful. Breathing fresh air and enjoying nature will do you a world of good. However, for weight loss, the nutrition does the heavy lifting, so to speak. For burning calories, it's something like 80 percent nutrition and 20 percent everything else.

The big, hairy gorilla is 100 percent emotional or comfort eating that overrides our good choices for both nutrition and exercise. Something happens around us, and it's like pulling a trigger that forces us to put something in our mouths for comfort. Until we address that mechanism, it does not matter how strong your willpower or resolve. When that is triggered, there is almost nothing you can do to stop yourself from hitting the candy bowl, the refrigerator, the pantry, or snack or beverage bar. It's so automatic that we hardly notice it. And it works. Somehow, it calms, soothes, de-stresses, comforts in the moment. In that moment.

Consider every diet you've tried. Initially, they go well. Then life sets in. Various liquids, capsules, and tablets do suppress physical hunger, and then you find yourself standing in the pantry or in front of the refrigerator looking for something anyway. Or the diet gives no limits on certain foods, so you eat them with abandon even if you are not hungry.

It's not hunger that drives that behavior.

It's an emotion, an experience, a habit, a need that you know but don't yet recognize or know how to resolve. Perhaps it's a need we cannot even articulate. There is no way around dealing with that. If we leave it as it is, we'll get the results we always have, and in another five years or 20 pounds, we'll still be looking for the magic potion to make the fat fall off.

The good news is that if you disarm that trigger, defang that beast, deal with the source of that behavior, it saves a ton of calories—and we have control over that choice again. And yes, it can be done. We may need a little help from a counselor, coach, or someone we trust, but we can meet that goal. Again, it's not instantaneous, but it will come as we choose it.

Change is often triggered by loss or frustration, and when my grandmother passed away, I had a heaping helping of both. She and my mother, who'd preceded her in death, had lifelong struggles with their weight, and I was following dutifully in their footsteps.

I wanted change. I didn't want to hit 50 struggling to lose that last 20 to 25 pounds yet again. I had just over a year. I set a reasonable goal—maybe not my ultimate goal, but it was a healthy weight for my body type, shape, and height.

Honestly, the first few months weren't too productive, but I was looking for something as I struggled with hunger pangs. I found lots of good information and, seriously, all it takes is following the blinkin' diet, right?

It wasn't the diet.

I could follow the diet religiously for a few days or weeks, and then something would happen, and I'd find myself standing in the pantry or in front of the refrigerator searching for the foods that would ease my pain du jour. The real pain came when I stepped on the scale a few days later and saw my hard work had evaporated. I'd be so mad, so frustrated with myself.

The diet had been working, and the real issue was solely how I coped with things that triggered comfort eating. I had to find a way to comfort myself without using food or drink as my security blanket. It took time and plenty of struggle. Changing habits is not for the faint of heart, particularly when they are lifelong habits. It took practice. I made some poor choices amidst the better ones. However, once I worked out my "stuff," I no longer had to stuff down my emotions and follow it with a food chaser. Not that I didn't like the foods I had always loved, but some were less tempting than they had been in the past. I was less vulnerable to eating too much or mindlessly.

When I faced the issue rather than trying to hold it under control, or when I examined it rather than covering it over, when I felt the emotions rather than trying to hold them back, I didn't require quite so much soothing. There was less damage, and I didn't feel so bad nor later so guilty.

My mantra became, "Face your stuff; don't stuff your face."

The Magic Bullet

There is a magic bullet for weight loss, and you already know how to use it. In fact, you've likely been using it for a long time unaware of what you were doing or how you were utilizing it.

The magic bullet of weight loss is the power of your intention.

Assess your intention for this goal. What do you want most? Truly. Write it down so you can see it in stark reality. What do you want?

How much do you actually want it?

Honesty is important here. There are many things I'd like to do or to be, but the requirements to get there may be greater than my desire. If I could magically acquire the skills or knowledge without working at it, I'd be totally on board, wouldn't you? Things just don't work that way generally, and it doesn't work that way with our food choices.

I know that feeling of wanting to want to but feeling incapable or minus the necessary motivation. My motivation to accomplish the task feels a little trapped in the ether. Shifting that gear can feel like a monumental task, and yet even the slightest pivot can harness our intention.

Maybe we can't cope with the thought of losing X number of pounds. It's overwhelming. What about five? What about making good choices for today and only today? Or only at the next meal? Or only one week? Identifying and accomplishing one task toward the goal is sometimes all we need to get us moving in the right direction. Create other goals later.

If you don't really want to reduce, it's okay. You can make that choice and, once you make it, own it. Allow yourself to be comfortable with that decision and the size you are. Your value doesn't lie in your reflection in the mirror. Once you've settled with the issue in yourself, the opinion of others will not matter so much. It's still your choice.

We may blame a particular diet for our challenges, but with the testimonials that come with every pitch, we know it's not the diet itself. It's the thousands of little choices we make that work either for or against our goal. Progress toward a goal has curves, straightaways, and cutbacks. We think it ought to be a straight line, don't we? Yet what we learn in downhill slides and struggling back to the path is invaluable. It's not easy to find the way back, and sometimes we need a compass when we get off track.

Getting clear on that goal, why it's important, and having a vision of yourself reaching that goal provides a measure, a compass. Here's an exercise: Make your vision of yourself reaching your goal vivid. What will you be wearing, where are you, what do you see, taste, and hear? Are there particular people treating you in a particular way? When you walk into a room, what happens? Deck this vision out in all your amazing glory.

Are you feeling the positive effects of that? Allow yourself to relish the good feelings.

Make that good feeling your compass. Every decision or choice that takes you toward that is fine. If it takes you away from that, you may want to reconsider whether that choice would be a worthy detour or get you completely lost. It's your choice.

Is that triple-sized cookie consistent with your intention? Will that doughnut or double martini make you feel good enough to last when you no longer quite fit into that outfit? Does either create the lasting comfort or stress release you seek? Will it resolve the issue?

Whether you're a bit lost or simply wanting to assess progress, always check your compass.

Shifting into a weight management program doesn't have to be wholesale and instant change. Small changes create sustainable changes. Consistently making more good choices in one or two areas will have a greater impact than periodically emptying your home of foods that are no longer "allowed." We can live with small changes, a few at a time; and soon those little adjustments become the "go-to" choice. That's real change.

Change begets change, and it's a transformational process. In that year, I excavated my heart that had been buried under a pile of expectations, failures, half-hearted attempts, poor habits, a range of unproductive beliefs, and mountains of woulda/coulda/shouldas. Before I hit my goal weight, my self-esteem was healing, and my authentic self was coming up for air, and she didn't need copious amounts of peanut butter or chocolate to manage life.

I hit my goal weight in the week before my 50th birthday. That was fun, but my greater joy came in the ongoing quest to reshape my life. Without all the distractions of negative self-talk, self-sabotage, and poor self-esteem, I was free to learn new pathways. I discovered tools I possessed already. I discovered gifts that I could share and nurture, which brought all the comfort, purpose, and joy I sought, and it didn't send unwanted surprises to my scale. I still needed comfort and stress relief, although not as often, and I found more effective ways to get it.

The usual ricochet from hitting a goal that took me back up five to 10 pounds changed to two to five pounds, and soon that dissipated to a very normal variation of a pound or two week in and week out. I was done with diets!

I was not done with making good choices. We know that if we return to our old ways of eating, the weight comes back from wherever it went—and it often brings several very pesky friends with it. Therefore, a key to maintaining a loss is making consistently good choices with the occasional detour into that indulgent food rather than making the indulgence the norm. No foods are banned with this method. I still have my favorite foods, but I have them now and again, indulging once a week, month, or year depending on what it is and how it affects me. We can enjoy anything if we manage our consumption of it.

Isn't it interesting that it's hard to hear that?

Feel that resistance rise? Feel the panic that perhaps you'll never again get to have your favorite food even though it clearly states no food is banned? *Oh, maybe that's a trick. Once I name my favorite food, in subsequent pages it will be coated with shame to get me to ban it myself. I'll be relegated to celery sticks when others have French fries! At the next holiday meal, I'll be ostracized from the celebration because I can't have XYZ—that's just not acceptable! Mind, I'll feel partly virtuous that I won't have to diet afterward but also so envious of the feeling of eating with abandon all the sumptuous offerings on the table. What's the fun in that? That's not life. And I'll just end up back here again because you just can't do life without _____.*

Breathe.

There is no trick.

We quickly spin out of control when limits are suggested. There is something within us that demands full freedom of consumption and, in our heart of hearts, we feel there really should be no consequences to that freedom. *Please don't make us suffer the consequences. Please.*

Indeed. Would that it were that easy.

We know there are consequences—I had 40 years of consequences. Now, however, I make better choices. That doesn't mean I don't enjoy my favorite holiday foods, but I choose the ones I actually enjoy and *enjoy* them. I learned to taste things, and I was surprised that some foods I'd long consumed weren't really that good.

I loved peanut butter cups. Even after I'd pared down my snack foods, I allowed peanut butter cups as an indulgence now and again.

Then I decided to evaluate them. It was an Easter Sunday. I breathed in the joy that is the mixture of chocolate and peanut butter. It connected me to so many good memories. I cut the "fun size" piece into four bites. The satisfying resistance of the knife as it sliced through the dense peanut butter, the scent rising, and the bits of chocolate that broke off and dotted the plate were so very familiar. I put a piece in my mouth and let it melt, lifting it on my tongue to the roof of my mouth, flavor spilling across all my taste buds.

Something was a little odd, but maybe the chocolate to peanut butter ratio wasn't right. I tried the second, but it was no good. My memory and the reality were at odds. I gave the pieces to my husband along with the rest of the bag. The magic was over, and I was incredibly surprised.

Shocked might be a better word. And disappointed. My favorite "candy bar" was no longer as good as I remembered it. What else doesn't taste the same as I recall?

For holidays now, rather than piling a plate, I make choices to enjoy the foods I like and leave the others. It was a little painful as the food was connected with memories. There again, the family has jettisoned several customs and foods that no longer fit our tastes or preferences, so it's no different. The memories remain. Just the food is different.

Apply that to the average Tuesday and the average lunch or vending machine snack, and consistently make choices that work for you. Consistency rewards effort. The thousands of little choices we make each day have great impact. Make more good choices and fewer indulgent ones, and make those indulgent choices what you most want. Then enjoy every bite. It's a place to start.

Shifting Gears

My grandmother passed away in September 2011. When my mother passed away in 2003, I soothed myself with food and drink, and I didn't want to do that again. I desperately missed both of them, and I could eat myself to death or I could take that impulse, that energy, and put it toward something that worked for me. That was the beginning of my journey to deal with my issues. Food had never effectively worked, although it was a quick soother, and at the time, I couldn't see another way to make myself feel better in the moment.

With a little help from a friend, I brainstormed a list of activities or experiences that effectively soothed me and didn't involve food. Want to give it a shot? List things that you can do in a couple of minutes as well as a longer activity, suited to the time you have available. Your list will fit you, but mine included a walk, certain music, pulling weeds in short spurts (not a long gardening session), playing with the dog or cat, or watching a short but funny video of pets.

My husband, Michael, can tell when I'm watching funny animal videos. He says the laughter is deeper and more infectious—and I say it's more effective than anything I could eat.

I also enjoy a quick video or card game, working on a jigsaw puzzle, turning a piece of wood on my lathe, or other creative building—okay, honestly just about anything creative does me the world of good. Quieter pursuits like looking through a kaleidoscope, organizing a drawer or shelf, deep breathing, watching birds or squirrels outside, a quick view of social media (note the quick), researching a topic I find interesting, and others are soothing. Sometimes, I simply sit and just be. I may let my mind wander where it will or count my blessings or try to think of nothing at all. I'm present, and that's enough. Some would call this meditation, and I suppose it is. Just don't make it too complicated. At its core, meditation is about stilling your mind and simply being present to where you are. Just breathe and "be" for a few minutes.

Having a list of activities or experiences from which to choose gives options. Food isn't the only soother. We've merely allowed it to be our go-to choice. There are many other options that will work just as well, be just as available, and will more effectively feed our hearts. Make a list. Get creative and discover as many options as you can for your internal soothing.

For Your Consideration

What do you truly want?

How much do you actually want it?

What's your story of emotional/comfort eating or other form of overeating?

With what words or phrases do you shame yourself?

What event or experience will throw you into an overeating tizzy?

How do you normally respond?

Which foods will you taste to see if you still actually like them?

Make a list of options for activities or experiences that will soothe you when you are upset, sad, mad, depressed, bored, frustrated, or otherwise in need.

For a free gift and further resources, visit
FreeGift.PackYourOwnBag.com.

I can help you deal with the emotional mosquitoes,
AND you still have to apply the repellant.

CHAPTER TWO

Emotional Eating

Quick Start Guide: Things That Work

To slow yourself down while eating, put your fork down between bites, and take time to chew. There's no rush. Maybe try using your non-dominant hand to handle that fork.

Chew every bite thoroughly—squeeze every bit of flavor out of it rather than chewing fast and swallowing quickly. If you love it, take time to enjoy it.

Pay attention when you're eating rather than downshifting to autopilot because you've always eaten this way. Autopilot is only safe when there are no known dangers, and what family gathering, buffet, office, or late night fridge raid is without known as well as unknown dangers?

Create a criteria list for foods: Why eat stuff you don't enjoy? If you don't like gelatin-based cheesecake, why would you waste the calories? If you don't like "margarita mix" and this particular bar or restaurant uses a mix, skip it. Make calories count—save them for what you enjoy.

Eat when you're hungry, but stop when you reach satisfaction. Satisfied will be full when your brain catches up.

When you have one of those moments when you can't say no to a food, then give the food the same physical honor you're giving it emotionally: Lay the table with a cloth or placemat, a nice plate or a crystal stemmed glass, using a utensil and a proper napkin, and be seated. If it's that important to you, eating it quickly at the sink hoping no one will catch you is deceptive and even disrespectful. Own it. Be honest with yourself, and enjoy eating or drinking that food or beverage in that moment. No guilt, no self-loathing, no hiding. Squeeze all the flavor out of it, and enjoy it. Once you treat it with respect, you'll likely enjoy it more and need it less often.

From mother's milk to bottles to pacifiers, in the early years, crying or upset children are soothed with putting something in their mouths. It's effective—soothing, comforting, reassuring, and it works almost every time.

At some stage, the pacifier disappears, and children often cry and ask for it. Cry? No, they beg for it. They cry themselves to sleep at night and beg for it in the daytime, an adjustment fraught with tears.

Parents are teaching an invaluable skill for life. We must learn to soothe and comfort ourselves without a pacifier. Once the child sees new options that work for them, they have no desire to return to the pacifier. They hadn't known other options were available, and they couldn't imagine the possibilities awaiting them or envision the freedom of being pacifier-free. They just want what they had, what had comforted them, what they knew.

Some of the adjustment may involve a substitute—thumbs, nails, pencils or pens, stir sticks, straws—all soothe even if they still tie comfort to putting something in the mouth. Then come the chocolate chip cookies baked "to make you feel better." We celebrate or commiserate with pizza or ice cream following a little league game, reinforcing oral soothing. Fast-forward through adolescence into adulthood, through all the foods and beverages that you seek when you need comfort from whatever ails, and say hello to being an emotional eater.

You are not alone or unusual. Western culture perfected it. A candy bowl sits in the middle of boardroom tables. Speakers engage interest by tossing wrapped candies to people who answer questions. Corporations have snacks freely available and visible to employees. Receptionists keep an open bowl of candies or mints. Maybe they've added some healthy alternatives, but clearly the Western creative and analytical minds run on having something to put in our mouths. Even a coffee stir stick will do. It's as if we find it easier to access our intelligence and creativity if mouths are occupied.

It's something we've learned to do as naturally as we've learned the lingo of our lives and work, and yet they are still substitutes, a way to soothe and comfort. Like the infant who can't see other possibilities, we've grown so accustomed to feeding our stress, sadness, frustration, and anger as well as joy and fun that we don't see the possibilities for meeting our needs in a different way. Or we don't believe they will meet our needs. Yet.

Putting something in our mouths never actually meets the deeper need, and the evidence of comfort food stays on our bodies like a warm blanket. As long as we keep seeking that comfort, the blanket stays whether or not it fills our need or creates new ones. Like the pacifier, we don't want to let it go, yet if we do not let that go, we won't see the possibilities. If we find a way to soothe and comfort ourselves within us, we no longer need the evidence of the blanket of fat we carry.

There are effective ways to meet our needs, and as we seek them, we find a world of possibilities. It's hard holding on through the initial shock of it—change is hard, whatever our age—and yet that frees us to explore the adventure of a lifetime. It will take some work, some intentional choosing… and perhaps tears and tantrums will follow for a time.

Yes, but that chocolate mousse would just make me feel so much better right now! Okay, so it won't, but it will make this moment better.

Will it?

Yes, in some ways. Yet that initial relief is so quickly followed by guilt and remorse, isn't it? The shame/blame/guilt triplets jump up out of nowhere and create more negative feelings, and self-sabotage sends us running again to the refrigerator, snack box, or bar to soothe even when we know we'll regret it in the morning.

That soothing food doesn't work ultimately. It may dull the momentary pain or frustration and then create a backlash of more pain and frustration. Emotional eating uses food as a bandage, an adhesive bandage, and the food adheres to our hips, thighs, back, and backsides. Ripping it away stings for a moment, and then with a bit of air and time, the wound heals.

Genuinely Hungry

When you are genuinely hungry, eat. Hunger is a signal that your body needs something. It just may not be a triple cheeseburger, ice cream, or a pound of chocolate even if they are the nearest and easiest options. That gnawing in your stomach is a signal, and our bodies give us signals to make a change. The key is in how we react to that signal.

Nature says we must find fuel just as we fuel our cars. The car doesn't get excited when I pull up to the gas pump. "Oh yippee! Regular unleaded headed for my tank! Can't wait, can't wait, can't wait! I'll gulp it down, and maybe I'll need a top-off later this afternoon just to savor that scent and feel the cool cascade down my throat."

It sounds ridiculous for a car, but when we're thinking in terms of the vehicle of our bodies… just think of your favorite meal. Italian?

Mexican? Steak and baked potato? Ribs with barbeque sauce? Oh, just go for the cake! The spicy aroma wafting from the kitchen toward you, the sounds of laughter and plates and glasses clinking together, the warmth from the oven pervading the room . . . you can almost taste it, can't you? And if it's coming up soon, can we not easily imagine every detail?

Salivating yet?

Food is fuel. It's not joy, comfort, or even effective satisfaction. Food is fuel. Granted, foodies have excelled at the tastes and mouth-feel of their gastronomic creations as well as creating great entertainment from its preparation. Our fascination with television programs featuring professional chefs may help us to be more creative in our own cooking, and that can be a good thing. Learn new cooking skills, be creative with ingredients or presentation, play with the macronutrients to fit your body's needs while making it taste great. It may now be delightfully packaged fuel, and yet food is still simply fuel.

But it doesn't feel that way when you're in the midst of an emotional roller coaster, and we've given it more meaning, different meaning, than it rightfully deserves. We've allowed it to become our go-to pacifier, and our culture reinforces and encourages it.

Think about that one or maybe two people at your workplace who do not join in for food fests. "Oh, go on—have a bite/drink. We're all doing it." We make it camaraderie or maybe misery loving company. When our gas tanks are full, we don't coax them to take in just a little more. When our vehicles run on regular unleaded, we don't try to give them diesel or even premium. There's no social shame in giving your car what it needs for optimum performance even if all the other cars in your garage or at the gas station are getting another type or amount. We've made food one of the elements of being part of a group, an element of quality for which we judge those outside the group—as in those who do not join in or do not agree with our preferences and proportions. It's silly, but it's part of our group thinking. From diets to barbeque, holiday stuffing to the proper form for clam chowder, we all have opinions about what others eat, how, when, or what they do not consume.

Intentionally adjusting to good choices around food is real satisfaction that lasts. It's an accomplishment that fuels more satisfaction and satisfaction in multiple areas. All the joy, none of the wrap-around guilt.

Making consistently good choices for food and soothing ourselves in a different way can be as natural and easy as establishing good daily hygiene. That's something we choose, and we enjoy the mundane but pleasant benefits. Perhaps there are days we choose to skip a shower, and yet we return to our routine before long, partly because we enjoy the benefits and partly because we loathe the consequences.

Making smart choices consistently may not yet feel natural, but it can. After a lifetime of choosing based on a combination of hunger, desire, emotions, and autopilot, which are always intertwined with guilt, it may take repetition, but the result is encouraging. It feels good to continually make good choices because you choose to, even if we stumble once in a while. Making one good choice will put us back on the path, and when we make good choices 80 percent of the time, the results are evident.

Losing the Pacifier

Face your stuff, don't stuff your face. It's a bit in your face, maybe pejorative, and yet it's truthful and can be helpful. Scarfing down a candy bar or packet of cheesy crackers may feel more immediately effective. We justify our actions by saying this isn't the moment to let that emotion affect my task or job; and after this pop-up storm passes, it will be over, we think. We'll sort this issue out later, we say, and yet we never find time to deal with the source, to resolve the issue. It's just a normal part of life to eat when we need comfort, isn't it? Everyone has stuff, we rationalize. Managing the symptoms is easier than confronting the stuff that drives our coping mechanisms, and yet ultimately healing or repairing the damage that created the coping mechanism would be so much more effective.

Yet we live with the damage, which creates more pain. If we can't say no to a food when we aren't physically hungry, can't stop eating something we don't even really want anymore, or find ourselves unable to make good choices or control ourselves during emotional or stressful situations, we're not just looking at symptoms. They are chains that bind us. They are a blinking light of brokenness, and we are captive until we heal.

Yet we don't. We may not even believe it's possible.

Not dealing with the source of the issue is costing us both time and money, and costing us dearly. It's no secret. The latest figures on the impact of obesity in the United States alone are staggering, and the World Health Organization has declared obesity a global epidemic. Health care costs for issues related to obesity are soaring along with incidence of heart disease, diabetes, stroke, debilitating joint issues, and even certain cancers. Many of these issues are preventable with behavioral adjustments, with balancing our food intake with our body's needs.

Taking the time to deal with the issues that drive the behavior means we no longer need the food chaser. After years of stuffing my emotional baggage, I can tell you that unpacking all that and being free is an amazing feeling, almost like awakening from a bad dream and realizing all the awful images and experiences that felt so real a moment ago have vanished. The dreams weren't real, and we wonder why we ever thought they were.

Exit Strategy: Identify True Need

What do you need? Food is the substitute, and it works in the moment, but the need remains because it hasn't been met. What do your heart, mind, emotion, and/or body need in that moment? We are complex creatures, and we feel stress when something is awry—we don't feel we're performing adequately (or perfectly), someone is demanding something from us in the moment, the contract is on the line, there is a deadline, we don't have control and therefore can't fix the problem, the unknown is towering over us, memories haunt and become bigger, hairier beasts that we can no longer stuff under the bed of our emotions, or that diagnosis frightens us.

Feel that stress just reading that list?

That stress/discomfort/anxiety is a signal that you need something. What is it? Truly. What does your heart need? Can you identify even a piece of it?

Do you need comfort? Soothing? Information? Someone to talk to? Someone to rescue you from a situation or guide you to a safer place emotionally? A hug? Affirmation or encouragement? What is it that your heart needs? Where can you get that right now?

I often found myself standing in my pantry or in front of the refrigerator staring, searching, wishing something there would do the trick. I knew nothing there would really help, but I looked anyway. It still happens once in a while, but now I ask myself the question, "What do I need right now, and how can I get that?"

This will take time and practice—and maybe a little help or a few creative life hacks until you realize you've regained control. We know what the need is, but sometimes it's like we're fumbling around in the dark, there are too many possibilities, or we have a strong attachment to habits so that we can't see where to begin. Food is easy, and it may be the nearest tool to beat back the feelings that threaten to overwhelm us.

I don't have time to analyze that right now—did you miss the part about the deadline?

Absolutely. That moment may not be the best time to figure out the triggers, causes, or origins, so make a time later when you can. Get your calendar, and do it now. Schedule time to figure out the issue, and show up for that appointment. We can't simply ignore our behaviors or emotions and expect the results to change.

There is another option. Let go of the idea of sorting out your weight management goals if you prefer to hold onto those habits and choices, and schedule time for being sidelined by these issues in other ways. The certainty is that if you don't deal with the emotions and triggers, the gremlins from your feelings will continue to jump up and bite you at the most inopportune times. Then you'll lose time by having to sort that out. It's okay to choose to punt your goals, but recognize it is a choice you are making rather than being the victim of your metabolism or situation.

Feeding our hearts will starve the stress of its power to drive you. If you get what you actually need, then all the substitutes are exposed as the tasteless cardboard they are.

Feed Your Heart, Starve Your Stress

Think of the many films about some hotshot who somehow lands and is forced to stay in a small town devoid of the big city comforts to which he/she is accustomed. The story is the journey of discovery, or rediscovery, of his true self, his heart, and what matters most. All the obstacles he faces peel back layers he has acquired. He didn't intend to get so far from his heart, but life beat up on him, and thicker skin helped him survive. Now he's blasting through town in a hot car, frantically trying to get to the place he is required to be, and life trips him up again. This time, however, it's deliverance.

Excavate you. If you are no longer encumbered by all the stuff that has buried you, you can stand up, shake yourself off, and just be you. How would that change how you feel and relate to food? Can you remember what you might be like? Like a well-worn pair of shoes, we sometimes don't realize how worn out they are until we replace them with a new pair. The comparison between old and new is ridiculous, and somehow we hadn't noticed. What would your renewed self be like?

And we hold onto some of our stuff in the same way, just like the child with the pacifier.

So much of traditional counseling gets stuck in seeking the source of our pain. We are hurt because of past experience, of a traumatic experience, abuse, and sometimes unintended wounding. We can find it, recognize its impact, but that doesn't deliver us. There is no healing in just feeling and expressing your pain. It may be cathartic, but it isn't healing. We can cry and rage forever, but if we are not willing to release it, we will be stuck with it forever. Dragging it with us in our backpack of experience—that grows to proportions and weights we can't believe—weighs us down and saps our strength. It beats the life out of us.

My grandmother made wonderful bread. She tried to teach me, but I worked it too hard. I kneaded, and kneaded, and kneaded. There came a time to stop kneading, and she knew the moment. I did not. I worked up some really good muscles, but the bread was never edible. We have to stop kneading... and needing... the dough of our pain. Work the dough appropriately, and let the loaf rise, bake, and be gone. We have to release it to be free.

Excavate—brush away the dirt, extract the pieces that work, dump the stuff that no longer fits you or your life. Some parts need cleaning to be adequately assessed. Some pieces need professional assessment and support, and yet much simply needs to be considered in light of your lifestyle and life stage and either organized or thrown out, redistributed, or recycled. Some are treasures to be valued if you dig down far enough to free them.

What's left? Once you stand up from all that, is it such a beast that needs taming or defanging? Or can you simply walk free, choosing the parts you want to take away?

When you unearth your true self, the best of yourself, you will find tools you need to conquer any challenge as well as gifts that are uniquely yours to share.

Then what of food?

It seldom works to soothe again, but then why would you want to go back to that old habit? It was ineffective, wasn't it?

A Simple Plan to Discover What Your Heart Needs

First, breathe. We do get caught up in the moment. What is your posture at this moment? When stressed, we seem to shrink into ourselves, and that tends to alter our breathing. A few deep breaths will relax the body. It's a simple thing, but it reduces stress, can be practiced anywhere, and costs nothing.

As you're walking through your day, feeling the stress or any negative emotion that has historically driven you to eat for comfort, take a moment to consider the emotion and how it feels to you. Before reaching for something to put in your mouth, take a deep breath and feel that emotion. Hold it tight, and let it pervade your body for 30 seconds.

What happens next?

Does it increase? Or does it dissipate?

The situation will not likely change, but you will. Like pulling our car to the side lane or on the shoulder to let a speeding car pass, and then we pull back on and keep driving while the car flies off into the distance. Without them riding on our bumper, shining their lights in our rear view mirror, and bearing down on us, we can relax and drive on at our own pace.

That moment of letting the feeling pass through often gives us clarity. Then we can see what our hearts really need in that moment. Once that initial surge of "stuff" washes over us, we can shake our heads and settle out all the noise, then make a better choice.

Now, what do you actually need? The first thing that comes to mind is likely true for you. Don't edit, just recognize it.

Maybe we need a quick walk down the hallway and back. Maybe we need to write something down for later or talk it out. Maybe we need to send that stress back to its source. Maybe we just need a second to think clearly, or some music, or help, or a chat with the dog, or some physical expression/exercise, or a hug—or whatever else uniquely fits you.

Perhaps you need to accomplish something, anything else. Keep a running list of tasks that take only five minutes or so. Pick one and do it, check it off your list. What you need is distinctive because you are. Learn what you need.

If after five to 10 minutes, the only thing that will help you still turns out to be that calorie packet, then that may be what you actually do need. That's instructive as well.

This practice will get easier the more you do it, and it's an effective way to begin facing your stuff without falling back on the old ways of mindless eating.

Shifting Gears

My golden retriever's ACL surgery helped me make a ritual out of a morning walk. His rehab started with three five-minute walks, and we worked up to an hour three times a day. After walking him an hour three times each day, an hour one time seemed like nothing.

A decade or so and another dog later, I go early, and my phone streams material that works toward my greater potential. A podcast, audio book, recorded webinar, a study, sometimes music—the only real criteria are that it feeds my heart while allowing me to be alert to what's going on with my dog and the environment. I get a good walk, a little fresh air, the joy of observing wildlife, connection with my dog, and some inspiration or challenge. Sometimes it helps me work out stuff. As my body is in motion working on my physical strength, my mind and heart can work on issues, bringing knowledge and clarity. It's a good start to my day.

For Your Consideration

What foods do you use as a soother?

What do you need? When food is the substitute, what do your heart, mind, emotion, and/or body need in that moment?

If you were no longer encumbered by all the stuff that has buried you, how might you be different?

Are you comfortable just being yourself? How would that change how you feel and relate to food?

Face your stuff so you don't have to don't stuff your face.

CHAPTER THREE

Unpacking the Issues

Quick Start Guide: Things That Work

SLOW DOWN. Take time to enjoy your food. I know, in school they only gave us so much time for a meal, and that seemed to set the pace for the rest of our lives. Hurry! Finish before the bell rings—join the clean plate club or brace for that disappointed look on the face of the teacher you wanted so badly to please.

Or perhaps it's a later pattern—running to this meeting or that, trying to (again) please an authority figure or meet your numbers. However, when it's possible, try enjoying the food you claim to love so much. Chew every bite. Squeeze every bit of flavor out of it rather than washing it down with a beverage. Take your time, and put your fork down between bites. Savor it. Notice that you are eating the food, so you remember the taste and mouth-feel. If you enjoy it while you're eating it, you won't need more later to replace what you didn't enjoy. Slow down, relax, and enjoy.

If you aren't going to take time to enjoy it, you may as well have celery sticks and plain lettuce.

Years ago, I had the opportunity to interview the authors of the latest diet book. I was young and a little cheeky, so I asked, "This is diet number 6,483. Is this The One?" To my surprise, without hesitation they said it was. They were certain their plan would work for anyone if they followed it, which is often true. It didn't work for me at that time and, honestly, I did not believe I could do without certain foods that were not compliant with the plan.

I'd spent years searching for a diet and nutrition plan I could live with long term, and I'd pretty much given up hope. Then "This One" came along, and I'd give it a try as I had with so many before it. My results were often mixed, but they did seem to work when I followed them to the letter, and the plan stopped working when I tried to modify them to include elements of old habits or favorite foods. Hmm.

Every diet works when followed. Whether they are keyed on calories or combinations of fat-protein-carbohydrates, timing, eliminating food groups, or fasting, every diet works for someone. Diets manage our menus as a guide to what the body needs. Remember "The One" that worked for you when you managed to lose efficiently for that period of time? Remember others that made you feel awful or left you hungry? Yes, we often know which diet works for us while making us feel good even if we still feel a little deprived and put upon to be managing our food intake. The problems come when we can't follow a prescribed menu for whatever reason—it's not the diet. It's us, our preferences, our emotional drivers.

Many articles on weight loss will name the usual suspects for why a diet doesn't work. Perhaps you're not getting enough sleep, your body is reacting to stress, you're not getting enough water or fiber, you have poor digestion, or you're not being careful enough with food choices. All are true at various times, but you know that already, and you've likely tried managing those elements while at least attempting to follow the menu.

Diet menus do not take into account the emotional short circuit. Maybe this food or a single serving of the item doesn't satisfy your hunger, or you get bored with the options suggested for this diet. You miss something you used to eat with abandon. Not saying anything about that desire for abandon, but seriously? A whole package? ... note my own sheepish demeanor... and I'm not alone. One of my clients confessed to eating a whole Sara Lee cheesecake one evening. We can't really explain those emotional short circuits that make no sense to us when we're staring at an empty container or serving plate and feeling the weight of it in our stomachs. However, we can sort out the triggers and learn to manage them.

At their base, diets are not only about a prescribed menu. The key to them is about effecting lifestyle changes. It's training. We learn what works for us and what doesn't, what satisfies physically and emotionally. Once you get to that goal weight, the idea is to stay there, not ricochet up a few pounds or slowly creep back up to the heavier weight. It's one of the life lessons for being an adult—responsibility means we may not be able to do the irresponsible things we did before, or perhaps we never could.

Sometimes we rebel against that responsibility. We choose to be responsible in other areas, and this is our point, our free zone, a refuge to do what we want when we want. That's one way to go, and you do get to choose when the consequences don't bother you enough to do something different. I'd wonder what's behind that, mind. Why am I so responsible in other areas and leave this one? What does that do for me? If it's so important to me, why do I dislike or hate the consequences and periodically torture myself by trying to undo them?

Another question revolves around control. Those with certain eating disorders realize that when their lives feel out of control, the one thing they still have some control over is what they put in their mouths. One friend flipped that coin to work for her benefit and health. Life was a bit out of control, and she liked having control, so she used it—she could control her food intake, and she didn't have to choose foods that would add to her waistline. She lost a significant number of pounds in a short time.

One of our realities is recognizing that eating an excess number of calories for one's body in a day, in whatever combination according to your weight management philosophy, will likely put your body in fat storing rather than burning mode unless you are a serious athlete.

Your body chemistry will dictate your personal fuel mix balanced with exercise, but generally, when we take in too much of the wrong things, the evidence is all over our face, hips, and waistline. The way to find that mix is to experiment. We know the diets that worked for us. Mind, doing the fat free thing worked for me initially, but I did not find it sustainable. It takes some effort to find the balance of nutrition that will satisfy and support a healthy weight. If we look at it as a puzzle, it may be more fun than drudgery.

What? A "diet" fun?

Why can't it be? I know, it's what we've always thought. How has that helped us? Thinking of utilizing a nutrition plan to work toward a goal as drudgery has created just that, hasn't it? I did my fair share, and maybe more than my fair share, of whining and moaning about my sparsely filled plate, no "fun" foods, and forcing myself to exercise. It was a self-inflicted torture that I made worse by thinking about it that way. Rethinking it into a puzzle sparked fascination. It was playful, and any task approached playfully tends to be more fun as well as effective. Give it a try?

With a new nutrition plan, we do get some new toys, foods, and beverages, and some of those can be hacked to decrease that fat storing mechanism. We also have a world of foods available that might be good replacements. When I say good, I mean something that is genuinely as satisfying as the food being replaced. I lived through the 1970s and saccharine in sodas. It fizzed. It had some sort of sweetness. It wasn't a Coke. In the 1980s, rice cakes did nothing for my need for a crunchy snack. I mean GOOD replacements. Oh, the joy that is a good coconut pancake or muffin! Had I only known!!!

I'm not gluten sensitive, but I do love some of the recipes. That muffin in a mug thing? WOW! Chocolate, vanilla, coconut, lemon, cinnamon—haven't quite worked out the carrot cake version yet, but it's a fun process, and the minute muffin is my new favorite breakfast that feels so decadent that I don't feel deprived. I will eat these muffins whether I need to lose or not.

Not that I get excited or anything.

Your favorites will be different, and that's the point. Find what works for YOU.

See the recipe for the Muffin in a Mug at the end of this chapter.

Four Keys to Weight Management

1. Know Your Body

Every creation that is the human body is different. We share some qualities, but nutritional science is so complex even doctors and nutritional experts do not agree on what works, so you must know your own body. You likely already know your caloric set point, as in how many calories you can burn in a day with and without exercise. I know my basic number and foods that maintain my weight and what will help me lose when I need to or maintain when I'm at a healthy weight. It takes a little focus and effort, but when I stay within my parameters, it works every time. Every. Stinking. Time. Dang it.

Learn your body and find what works for you. In the "Land of the Instantaneous," this may take some trial and error with documentation, but diligence pays off. What satiates you? What foods actually keep you satisfied between meals? Anything? What holds you for three hours? Anything hold you for four or five? What evaporates before you get out of the kitchen? Is there a nutritional plan you've tried before that worked well for you? That one that made you feel good and helped you lose the pounds? Most long-term dieters found one that worked, and then comes that feeling of "I'm tired of having to pay attention to this or restrict myself," and we return to eating whatever whenever, and the loss stops. Surprise, surprise.

Look at your current nutrition diary—or your best memory of what you eat. What do you know to be helpful? What do you know isn't helpful? Long-term weight management isn't about following a strict diet for however many weeks or months. It's about finding the nutritional construct that keeps you satisfied the longest and either helps you maintain or lose—or gain if need be. It's about knowing that AND being content to live with it, which gets into our emotional stuff.

2. Know Your Emotional Stuff

We usually know what sets us off toward over or impulsive eating—our triggers for comfort eating. You know what sends you to the kitchen to stare longingly into the refrigerator. Find ways to heal that or plan for how to manage it. Hire a coach or counselor if you don't think you can do this on your own, and so many of us can't. We need a little help to disarm those comfort eating triggers. We've accepted them for so long that they've simply become our automatic response that we hardly notice until we finish off that entire family-sized package of whatever. Those triggers can be disarmed, and it takes some effort, but the pattern can be broken. Once they are disarmed, we're free again to make a choice about a response to whatever has set us off.

Start with recognizing what you're feeling. Identify what you are trying to soothe. It sometimes feels like a big hairy monster, and yet when we actually turn the light on it, we can see the truth. Sometimes that alone will relieve the stress. Sometimes it's actually a big hairy monster, or a threat to our livelihood.

Whether it is a real physical threat or a stress-induced threat, the reaction in our bodies is simple chemistry. Hormones are released to help us deal with the threat. Physical threats require the physical response of escape, a burst of energy that burns calories. With a stress threat, we use mental and emotional energy rather than physical, but we are still left with the "need" for food even if we haven't burned the calories making a physical escape. Annoying, I know.

A physical threat could be genuine hunger or a nutritional need we haven't recognized that shows up as a craving. What are you actually looking for? We may interpret a craving for chocolate as a need specifically for chocolate, but the chocolate may be a package for a particular mineral in which we're deficient. Pregnancy sometimes creates cravings, and we've progressed far enough in our knowledge that we recognize the body is making its needs known. We don't dismiss it as indulging a pregnant woman or simply being good for the baby. The body uses the signal mechanism regardless of pregnancy, and we can learn to supply it with a food that works on our plan.

When it's a stress response, is what you need actually in THAT food item? No, of course not, and yet we've associated that food or putting something—anything—in our mouths with relieving that stressor. What do you need? Under stress, the brain wants glucose. That's its preferred fuel under stress, so plan, plan, plan for this. There are foods that will be on your plan that provide what you need. Identify and have it ready. When you know stress could be part of your day, plan around it just as you would choose your clothes to make you feel strong and/or comfortable or plan the way you speak for a stressful situation. This is part of your preparation for that big presentation, social gathering, client meeting, or anything else you do.

Dig deep for this. Do you want something sweet because there isn't enough "sweetness" in your life at the moment? Is it something salty because you need something that is engaging or provocatively stimulating in your life? Or do you need something with a vinegary or sour edge to align with a souring situation or to counter one that is sickly sweet? Or is it connected with your past? Someone gave it to you any time you were experiencing this kind of stressor. Take some time to identify what you're seeking, what it relieves for you, and why.

It has historically relieved and comforted you at least for the moment, but is that moment really long enough before you need another shot of it? Or is it more than adequate for you? Is it still adequate with all the attendant results and consequences? If it is, great. Keep at it. If it isn't, what could be a better option that will meet your need without damaging your ability to maintain your weight intentions? If you no longer had to counter the effects of that food indulgence, what else could you do with your calories, activities, and energy?

We also know our day-to-day stuff. Why do we feel cheated if someone else gets to eat more than we do? Or feel neglected if a really thin friend can eat a whole pizza, sugar all day, a bucket of ice cream, the two-foot-long hotdog/triple cheeseburger, a lunch made up of snack machine offerings, graze all day long, or have whatever food we are craving—but I can't? How is that fair?

It isn't fair. It just isn't. And that's not really the question. Why does it make us feel cheated? We accept differences in other areas like choices, preparation, location, or final result from occupation to lifestyle to weather. I live in Texas, and we don't have balanced seasons unless you call a six-month summer and fall blending into spring as balanced. Our leaves usually turn brown and fall off the trees in a couple of days if not overnight after a "blue norther" barrels down on us from Canada. Do I feel cheated when I see beautiful fall colors or pristine snow in pictures or on television? When I see a news report that includes people playing outside on a summer evening when we can sweat standing still even after sunset? Do people in North Dakota feel cheated when a Texas winter is sometimes only a couple of weeks long, if it shows up at all? We may long for the greener grass on the other side of that fence, but we accept it as part of our reality. Why do we apply the meaning of being "cheated" to food proportions?

Doesn't mean we don't want it to be true. I'd like to be taller as well as eat whatever whenever, and neither is likely to happen. Some things we simply have to accept or drive ourselves nuts trying to change the laws of nature. And buy a stepstool to reach top shelves.

It may be a question of metabolism, or it may be the choices they make as well as other things we don't see. I have a friend who will get all kinds of foods from the snack machine, but she never finishes a package. She will order the fattiest, highest calorie entrée off the menu, but she never eats half of it. If you grew up in the "clean plate club," that may set off a few issues. Take a deep breath and come back to the point. Calorie for calorie, she likely eats about the same as I do, but she has what she wants and has the ability to leave the remainder either altogether or for another time. Now why can't I do that? Why don't we choose to do that?

Is it discipline? Choosing to be less greedy? Is it a fear of scarcity? Definitely some envy going on, and that seldom has a positive outcome, does it? And we're talking about food, a plentiful resource in Western culture. We're not even talking about basic food but the extras, the fun and indulgent options that we've ascribed way too much power and importance in our lives. Reality check time, isn't it?

When we think of our food habits in those terms, how does it feel differently? Where could we even slightly adjust our habits, our thinking, our choices? Where do we need to shake ourselves out of the hypnotic attraction and make choices that will be better for us and meet our specific needs?

3. Know Yourself

You are unique in what works for you, what motivates you, and what you most need to help you reach your goals. I know I need some external connection to work toward my goals. I'll work all day to help you meet yours, but I lose the thread when it's for myself. It's not a flaw, it's just part of me, and I have to work with it just like I have to account for my short legs and high shelves. Therefore, I have to build in some connection, some external accountability, whether that's work or weight, hobbies or relationships, activities or accounts.

To motivate myself to do a more physically challenging workout, I joined a new gym with a circuit, and I learned if I got there at a certain hour, I could get it done in record time. I knew the guy who monitored it would be there, and I let it become an expectation (only in my mind, of course) that he was waiting for me. Daniel was waiting, so I was not going to let him down. Then I joined a group doing an online workout challenge, and I took on the responsibility of posting regularly, which motivated me to do the workout. From almost no workout other than my morning walk, I shifted into a consistent workout routine every week for a year. The clincher for me was having someone expecting me to participate. That's just me, and that's okay, and it's one way I can manage my intentions and thereby manage my goals. Your unique needs can be employed to help you reach yours more efficiently.

4. Know It's Not a Short-term Fix

Changing a lifetime of habits takes time. Plenty of diets promise you quick success, and it's great if you have made the lifestyle changes to support and continue your healthier choices. How's that worked out for you in the past?

Yeah, me too. It wasn't until I made consistently good choices and adjustments that I maintained my weight where I wanted it to be. The real "fix" is learning what works for you and to keep doing that rather than doing the diet tango—on, off, on, off, on, off. That doesn't mean we'll never ever again get to enjoy the triple cheese burger with fries or that decadent dessert. It means we don't do that daily or maybe even weekly. The 80/20 rule can apply here. If you choose healthy options 80 percent of the time with 20 percent not so much, that can work forever. Your percentages may vary, and it's important to know what works for your body, heart, and lifestyle.

Overeating

The body is a sophisticated piece of machinery. It adapts and changes based on external as well as internal factors. Aging and environment affect its performance. Nutrition can keep it running optimally or slow it down. Unlike most engines, if you over-fill its tank, it will hold it, expanding to accommodate the fuel whether or not it's good for it.

Everyone has a unique threshold of maximum capacity, and that capacity can vary. My mother-in-law has a dessert compartment. She may have had her fill of the main meal, but there's a little room left specifically for the sweet finish. She manages her intake of one course to allow space for another. Had I been so wise in the past, perhaps my weight would never have been an issue.

Overeating is something we do, but perhaps it's time to look at the merits, question our choices, and change that behavior. Holidays tend to test our capacity, and maybe a party or a favorite food will tempt us to overeat. Consider whether that's a significant part of the holiday for you or if it's simply an excuse to indulge. If it's only an excuse, that's okay as long as you own it. What does overeating do to enrich the experience? Is it connecting with someone? Is it part of the family dynamic? Grandma or Auntie will feel slighted if you don't eat enough? Or is it just something you've always done? Typically, such choices are driven by a long-term habit, simple gluttony, over-hunger, emotions/stress, or even sedating ourselves, and this drug doesn't last. However, once we identify our driver, then we can alter it.

Habit

Imagine the breakfast, lunch, snack, or dinner you most often choose. If you were to go to a restaurant, where would you go? Do you try different entrées or do you most often have the same meal? When you come in from a long day, what do you do first? Second? When something happens to upset or frustrate you, what do you do? If you are responsible for setting the menu, is there any pattern to your choices each day or week? How and when do you take your coffee or tea?

We are creatures of habit, and once a choice is set, it's often set forever—unless we consciously choose to do that task differently and continue to do it differently.

I don't like coffee. I have tried to like it, but I just don't. Friends have tried to find versions of coffee that I might enjoy to no avail. The flavor, even in small amounts, is unpleasant. Love the scent, don't love the flavor. I grew up drinking iced tea. I'd have an occasional cup of hot tea, which was pleasant, but it didn't become a habitual part of my day until I moved to the UK for a job in my twenties.

I was then immersed in a demographic that drinks a lot of hot beverages. Their average temperature is lower than where I had grown up in Texas, and the unaccustomed rain made it feel colder to me, so a hot cup in my hand was very welcome. They were perplexed at an American who didn't drink coffee, so I bonded with tea. However, I wasn't certain of how I "took my tea" as I'd never heard of adding milk to tea. In Texas, it was almost always served iced.

For the first six months, I tried out the various options to see what I liked best. My job entailed a lot of visiting people in their homes, so I tried tea as they served it for themselves. When I was on my own, I often began the day with black tea. By lunchtime, I would add some sugar. By mid-afternoon, I'd switched the sugar for milk, but by the end of the day I wanted it with both milk and sugar. Soothing comes in many forms.

The reality was that I liked it all four ways for different reasons, but over time, it was easiest to settle into one preference. It may have been a better practice if I'd checked in with myself each time to decide what I actually wanted, but for the sake of simplicity, I settled into taking tea with milk and one sugar. That became my habit for the next six years until I decided to change my preference to dropping out the sugar in deference to my waistline. Making that one small change was harder than I expected. It took a month for it to taste right to me, but after that, I never wanted sugar in my tea again. It no longer tasted right. It was no longer my habit.

We fall into habits with food and beverages. Sometimes we genuinely like certain foods made or complemented in certain ways. Sometimes we simply are not aware of an alternative or aren't willing to spend the time to find one. There's also the law of diminishing returns. A little sugar, salt, or pepper accents and enhances flavor, and over time the recognition of that accent seems less pronounced, so we add more. Cut out all salt, and you'll notice the difference, but over time, it will be less pronounced. Introduce more salt, and it will be very apparent.

When I arrived in the UK, I was very aware that sweet things were not as sweet as foods in the United States. When I returned to the States, my taste buds were overwhelmed with how sweet so many foods were. We adapt.

Habits streamline our activities because we don't have to think about them. We just do what we normally do—no thought, no decisions, simply autopilot choices. It's easy.

When we try to make an adjustment, sometimes it just doesn't taste right or we feel like we haven't really had what we wanted. We have to stop and think and evaluate rather than going with our "usual." It's awkward, and the transition takes effort. Many give it up as too much trouble. Case in point, consider New Year's resolutions. Resolving to make a change is a positive goal. Actually making that change takes commitment to the process as well as the change.

One key to weight management is evaluating our habits and choosing those that will support our goals rather than hindering them. It's not easy, and those around us may find it odd. "You've always taken your coffee with cream and sugar. Why would you want to change that now?" Your adjustment can be a threat, a betrayal, an annoyance, or a minor inconvenience to others, but for whatever reason, others are not always supportive when you want to make the smallest change. "Our family ALWAYS has X dish with X holiday meal. Or X dessert with extra cream/ice cream/X add-ins."

Word to the wise: Just don't mess with family holidays. Just don't. That's too emotionally charged and too fraught with landmines. There are more productive battles to fight.

Making changes takes time. Our brains automate. We've done it this way for years. Be gentle with yourself as you make changes, and know what method works best for you. Some will do better with one habit at a time, allowing one to be firmly in place before going on to the next one. Small doses of sustainable change create a lifestyle. For others, wholesale change works best, clearing the cupboards of every temptation, changing all recipes to support the new choices, and going hard at exercise six days a week. Know what you need and what creates self-sabotage, and that also will be different for everyone.

For whatever method, know that there may be bumps in the road. Some changes need more reinforcement than others. It takes time to break associations, ties, and automatic choices. Diligence is a great tool. Let the fog of the bump clear, then straighten your intention, and go at it again. Slow and steady is still progress.

Shifting Gears

I had plenty of habits, some useful, some not so much, so I created some new habits. One was that I only have sugar on Sundays. I'm a registered chocopath—which means I love dark chocolate—and I love the instantly addictive drug we call sugar. I was the one who went to school on sugar bomb cereal, wanted something sweet at break, after lunch, mid-afternoon, and after the evening meal. Love it. LOVE it. It was hard to get something too sweet for me. Combine sugar and chocolate, and I'm in ecstasy.

A meal never felt complete without something a little sweet at the end. It's no wonder I gained and lost the same 20 to 35 pounds over and over and over. Establishing the habit of limiting sugar to Sundays could have felt like punishment, but instead it gave me a boundary. When I'd find myself in the pantry looking at the chocolate chips, I reminded myself, "I only have sugar on Sundays." It became a mission, and that turned into an accomplishment.

Not that my Sunday became a pig out kind of day. I chose a portion, and I timed it to balance it with my blood sugar needs. I'm not diabetic, but once I extracted the constant flow of sugar, having sugar did have more of an effect on my body. I didn't eliminate all sugar, which is a really hard thing to do with all the added sugars in prepared foods, but I did intentionally choose where I took my sugars. After all, French fries were intended as a delivery system for ketchup, weren't they? No? Really? Any time I have something high in sugar, I have it on a Sunday, and I balance it with a protein to mitigate the effects on insulin production.

That one habit of limiting sugar to Sundays—along with a general rule of not accepting food offerings from the offices or marketers I meet through work—has saved me a lot of calories. In the offices I visit, there always seems to be a lot of sugar around—chocolate or candy bowls, doughnuts, and such. They always offer, and because of my habits, I can always say no and feel completely at peace with doing so. It's an effective temptation fighter. I offer more tips and methods for fighting temptation and breaking your same-old habits in Chapter Nine.

Muffin in a Mug

3 Tablespoons of some type or combinations of coconut, almond, or flax flour
1/8 tsp. baking powder
Pinch of salt
2 tablespoons water (or 3 if desired)
½ tablespoon coconut oil (oil of your choice)
1 egg
½ teaspoon vanilla
Sweetener to taste: 1 teaspoon to 1 tablespoon Stevia blend or sweetener of your choice
Stir together in mug or bowl, and microwave for 1 minute. Enjoy hot.

Variations:
1 Tablespoon of cocoa—warning: could be addictive
In place of vanilla, use lemon, almond, coconut, or another flavoring. Choose your favorite.
1 tsp. Cinnamon
1/2 tablespoon chia seed
Coconut or almond milk in place of water

For Your Consideration

Find what works for you. Get a notebook, a notepad, your smart phone, an app, or whatever method by which you can note your discoveries. You don't have to keep a food journal, but you can if it's helpful.

What foods are satisfying to you? Truly satisfying.

What foods keep you satisfied between meals?

What foods last for three hours? Four hours? Five minutes?

What nutritional plan worked well for you by helping you feel good and reduce your weight?

What foods seem to activate your cravings?

What can you eat, be satisfied, and leave alone?

What foods are "more-ish"? As in, you always want more of it or a measured amount leads to more than you planned?

What foods kick off a detour?

What MUST you have—can't live without it?

What situations send you straight to the kitchen, snack box, or drive through?

What are you feeling? What would soothe you without requiring food? Do you need someone to help you work through the thoughts and feelings around that situation?

As you play with your food, evaluate your satiety, and check your cravings, you'll discover a rhythm and perhaps a pattern. Once you find foods that serve as triggers for cravings, moods, or additional hunger, evaluate how often you can consume them without countering your goals.

"I am not a glutton; I am an explorer of food." Erma Bombeck

CHAPTER FOUR

Gluttony, the Culture–Approved Sin

Quick Start Guide: Things That Work

Craving Buster Remember your last great meal in vivid detail. This is almost counterintuitive, but it works. Remember the flavors and textures, the savory, the sweet, the creamy, the crunchy. Was any of it vinegary in the best possible way? Did every chew release all the spices to explode on your tongue? Or was it so smooth and velvety that you almost didn't need to chew as it coated your tongue with rich flavor?

Inhale the memory of the scent. Warm, spicy, inviting? Perhaps buttery with sugar or vanilla like fresh baked cookies? Home scents like cinnamon? Or fresh and salty or woodsy like your favorite holiday destination? Does it take you back to a specific place and time?

See the table setting and those who share this meal with you. See the colors, perhaps the sparkle of crystal or the casual comfort of the kitchen table. Who was there? Friends? Family? "Framily?" Recall the laughter and the intimacy, the comfort of truly belonging.

What was the first bite you chose? How did you select and order the offerings? Imagine the food you enjoyed most, and enjoy every bite. Savor the memory of the experience and how you felt.

Replaying it can satisfy the craving if you put your full effort into it. We replay lesser experiences often enough to affect our moods and feelings. A positive memory serves a more encouraging purpose. For all practical purposes, our minds do not know the difference between the experience and a mental replay. Think about watching a film with strong emotion. We can cry, be angry, and be elated watching someone else experience those emotions. We get in touch with emotions by watching others or replaying our own.

If you're not actually hungry but only bored, stressed, or emotionally hungry, this exercise can satisfy and bring relief. So take five minutes to relax, breathe, and remember.

It's not socially acceptable to point it out, so forgive this straightforward confession. Much of my weight issue was simple gluttony. I wanted to eat more than my body could handle. The food tasted good, and it soothed something within me, so I returned for seconds, thirds. I loved the feel of it in my mouth, and I particularly love creamy things. There's just something about it that I can't even explain, but the texture is my favorite.

What makes it hard to get a handle on is that overindulging, eating with abandon, gluttony was a common practice for my family of origin, particularly around holidays. It was part of the holiday, it was paying tribute to the cook, appreciating provision with gratitude, and it was fun. If you weren't stuffed, you hadn't really enjoyed the holiday.

One Fourth of July, my mother made ice cream, and it was an especially good batch. She made it after lunch, and we nibbled on it for the rest of the day forgoing a proper dinner and enjoying the ice cream. Ready for this? It was a six-quart freezer—a gallon and a half—and there were only four of us. There's no way to account for that beyond gluttony. Forgive me, I did sin. And I loved all 40 ounces of my portion. That's not a half-gallon tub of Blue Bell to myself . . . quite, but it would have been a significant dent in the carton. I wasn't repentant until the scale showed the increase. We didn't do fat-free or sugar-free in those days. No, this was whole milk with cream added along with whole eggs and copious amounts of sugar. Don't forget the toppings!

It may not be a quart of ice cream for you, but there are easy ways to take in over 1,000 calories. Restaurants now have a "Healthy Options" section of their menus that loosely translates to fewer than 600 calories, which is still a significant chunk of one's daily calorie allowance. Most entrees cross over 1,000 calories and others exceed the recommended daily allowance for the average female. Some restaurants have items that make a 1,500 entrée option look low-cal compared with others topping 3,000 calories. Granted, we may not consume all of it at one sitting. Of course, we wouldn't do that, would we? I spent years doing just that. Clean Plate Club!

Gluttony is a common practice in our culture. We don't call it that, of course, but it is an allowed vice or addiction. It's okay, and it's insensitive to speak against it—unless the evidence is observable on a red carpet with commentators looking on and snarking for TV cameras.

We love to eat. We do! We love to eat portions as served rather than a serving as our portion. Check out any celebration or time of grief, and food will be nearby if not the center of the gathering. Food is often the underpinning of the gathering. I tried to organize an event once that would not include food. The idea was shot down in committee with the justification, "Why would anyone come?" We go almost nowhere that food and beverages are not available in abundance.

We have super-sized our menus and made additional carbohydrates like bread or chips part of the standard service, a pre-appetizer. We don't even have to request it as we do with the formerly standard water. It just comes to the table. At an unfamiliar restaurant in London, a basket of bread was presented to the table and swiftly removed after Michael and I had both taken one of the variety of breads. We heard a few whispers from other tables when they were presented their bills, and when we received ours, we knew why. We were surprised by an extra line on our bill for the bread. It was standard practice in that restaurant to charge for the basket whether or not you finished it.

In other restaurants in the UK, Europe, and the United States, the specific cuisine's version of bread or chips are included as part of the experience. It has become so much a part of dining in many Western countries that we don't think about it. We just consume what's put before us along with the salsa, oil, butter, or other condiment that goes with it, calories and all. It's something to do until the appetizer or main course arrives.

It's less hunger most of the time and actually more of a habit, and increasing the diameter of the standard dinner plate according to trends has not helped our awareness of caloric intake. Our perception of space on the plate suggests whether or not we've been given an adequate amount of food, and if there is too much white space, we wonder if we're being shorted. One old trick of those watching their intake is to use a smaller sized plate to enhance the visual cue of a full meal. Use a luncheon plate rather than a dinner plate or a platter. The plate will be "full" much faster, and it will likely be more than adequate for your needs.

As our culture increased the frequency of going out for meals, the supply of restaurants increased along with the size of plates and portions. To maintain smaller price increases, we increased the size of the side dishes to fill those plates, and therefore we created a distortion in the size of standard portions. We don't satisfy ourselves with one serving—we often don't even know what a serving is. If we measure it out, it looks awfully small, doesn't it? Don't the ready-made "diet" meals look significantly smaller than many other frozen meals? Forget those made supposedly "man sized." It's not just the gender bias at the root of our objections.

Ever measured out the recommended one-half cup portion of starchy carbohydrate? Even if you measure it as the size of a tennis ball or a cupped handful, it doesn't look like much on the plate. Two cookies won't cut it; we need four or five. One half cup of ice cream looks like punishment or a kiddy portion. A four-ounce steak looks like we've been cheated. What cow only gives us four ounces of any steak? Isn't that whole steak nature's portion (along with a generous butcher)? When was an eight-ounce pour of soda considered a serving? That's like three gulps. The small order of fries, burger, and a soft drink should be from the kiddie menu and should be labeled only as such.

Ahem. Pardon my whine.

Resetting what our minds and eyes believe about portions will be a challenge given the amount of time we've reinforced them, but it's a winnable battle. Initially it may not feel like quite enough as you leave the table, and yet it's more than adequate for nutrition, and our previously indulged appetites will adjust to it just as our bodies adjusted to the larger portions and showed us via the scale or snug fit of our clothes. The adjustment is partially physical but even more mental and emotional.

In my family, there was a sort of pride in being able to keep up with the men, consuming as much food with as much enthusiasm as they did. We'd worked as hard as they had, so we ought to be able to eat as much, shouldn't we? "Can't you get around that?" or "Don't let it beat you. You can polish it off." It was wasteful not to consume what you were given.

As it was done, it can be undone. When I was assessing my personal nutritional amounts, initially I mentally toughed my way through smaller portions, reversing the idea from my experience. "Don't let it beat you. You don't have to eat that much or polish off that entrée if you're no longer hungry." Yes, it was a game I played with myself, but it fueled my quest.

I made it even more of a game. Granted, this takes time, effort, and awareness like reworking any habit, and thinking of it as a game made it more fun. Seriously, how much or little do I actually need to satisfy me? Focusing on satisfaction over a full feeling in the first 20 minutes helps because we know it takes 20 minutes for the brain to register the condition of the stomach. Could I be satisfied on less than a full portion? I could always have more if I wasn't. I'd stop after I'd eaten a certain amount and ask the question, "Am I satisfied? How about now? Or now?" If I wasn't satisfied with the portion, I enjoyed the indulgent feeling of going for seconds.

I played with different foods. What about this combination? More protein, fewer carbohydrates? Or more carbohydrates and less protein? Balance this, replace that? How did I feel afterward? What was my energy level the next day? Would a cup of [insert your favorite hot drink here] add to the warm and satisfied feeling at this meal or snack?

It took a week or so to discern my quantities, and if I'd misjudged, I reserved the right to either add in a snack or reduce the next meal to suit my hunger level. That's part of the game. We investigate what foods satisfy, how much we need, how long it will last us, and try different snacks to fill in a hunger hole when it appears. Certain foods will work for me that won't work for you because of the variations in our metabolic needs, but go with your instinct. The same snack I'd chosen as a child when I was hungry, usually cheese or nuts, will still—in appropriate portions—kill that desperate feeling and give me a moment to think clearly so ravenous hunger doesn't tank my management efforts.

If it doesn't sound very entertaining to you, think about how you learn any new skill, craft, or hobby. We often need instruction or help from others to learn how to do new things, and it requires some intention and practice to get good at it. The cooking programs show us how to make simple to complex recipes, offering tricks to pull it off and make it look pretty. We may not get it right the first time, but we practice the ones that taste good and then perhaps get more creative with the recipe. Figuring out your nutritional needs will take some practice and experimentation. Choose to make it fun and the motivation will join in.

Gluttony in Practice

Essentially, gluttony is over consumption of food, drink, or anything we can possess. It is considered one of the seven deadly sins in Christian culture, prohibited in Judaism, expanded beyond simple consumption to how it is consumed in Catholicism, considered a point of extravagance or waste in political circles, and Islam urges followers not to waste by excess.

Gluttony is a misplaced desire, elevated above other needs and the needs of others.

At a family lunch at my grandparents' place, my grandmother, mother, and aunt had been working in the kitchen for the second half of the morning preparing while the rest of us were out finishing up the morning ranch tasks, and we were hot and hungry when we hit the door to wash up. Because we'd be going back out after lunch for more chores, we were only required to have clean hands, and a wet cloth would suffice to sponge off the sweat so we wouldn't disturb those around us too much. On that day, the scent of baking rolls overpowered even the scent of my brother's sweat.

When washed, we met in the dining room, greeted by a table laden with just about every dish we loved. I know there was a tablecloth on the table, but it was only visible around the bottom half of the place setting. We gulped down some iced tea and awaited what we often considered the main course: The homemade bread rolls hot from the oven. There's nothing like that first taste—or the agony of waiting for the plate to be passed around. Dripping with the home-churned butter made from the milk from our cows, we sat for the first few minutes eating only bread, maybe even having another, mouths too full and happy to even ask for the serving dishes filled with other favorites to be passed around.

Might have been more than a little gluttony going on there—certainly was by the time we'd piled our plates high with meat, vegetables, and salads (not skinny salads, I should confess), and then we went on to at least two kinds of dessert. We would eat until we physically could not stuff anymore in and then retire to the den for some moaning on the floor before we returned to outdoor tasks or cleaning up the kitchen.

Our desire was for the rolls and all the other dishes my grandmother orchestrated with such love and skill, but we took it to a gluttonous level, particularly on national holidays that typically worked out to be three- or four-day food orgies.

You might be falling to gluttony if you:

- Eat beyond satisfaction

- Eat too fast

- Stuff your mouth and swallow rather than chewing each bite thoroughly, or you wash it down with your beverage

- Display physical evidence unexplained by a medical condition

- Prioritize your desire for food over relationships or activities

- Take more than your share

- Lack self-control around certain foods

- Settle into an "I don't care; I just want it" attitude

- This is a partial list for the purpose of recognizing the issue—not for use as a club to beat ourselves up. Recognizing an issue is the first step to changing it.

Over Hunger

We know that feeling. We are so hungry we could eat the house. Our backbone feels like it's rubbing a blister on the front of our stomach. Our stomach doesn't just grumble, it roars. The next thing we see that is edible is going in our mouths, no matter what, and we don't really care what it is or how much is available—we'll just stuff in whatever is available until we feel better or there is no more, whichever comes first.

Whether you are fasting for the health benefit or restricting calories for a diet or you've been tied up in a meeting or string of meetings too long, allowing yourself to get over-hungry without a plan for breaking the fast creates a boomerang for over-indulging. We often are filling an unknown—or perhaps known—void with whatever is readily available. When we get over-hungry, we lose perspective and judgment; we just NEED food. It's a biological necessity and response. That's no place to make good decisions about anything.

It happens to everyone at various times, so know what you need and what takes that frantic edge off your hunger. Keep healthy snacks where you can get to them. What works for you and can be your go-to choice if you get that hungry? This is where habit works for you. If you know what both works for you and is a viable option that can be available wherever you are, then even in an unplanned situation you know what will save you from a binge. Again, everyone is different. A portion-controlled bag of nuts or jerky in the car works for some, while a more carbohydrate rich portion-controlled bag of unsweetened cereal or crackers works for another. Individual portions of cheese, a single-serving protein bar, a small piece of fruit, an individual yogurt, or a small serving of vegetable sticks and a healthy dip will curb the manic munchies.

See what I did there with the portion-controlled, single-serving elements? It's not a "grab a meal." It's an effort to take the edge off that fog that ends in stuffing anything and everything to reduce the panic of being over-hungry. When that foggy panic clears, we can make good-for-us choices again. Know what you need.

It's curious that we will shop for hours or days to find just the right dress or blouse, THE one that fits us—our bodies, our colors, the occasion, our mood, our _____ body part to either camouflage or enhance. Yet we simply refuse to seek what our body, heart, or emotions need to truly fit us. We settle for a cookie, snack machine options, or whatever is left over from some company lunch—whether we like it or not—to stave off feeling hungry.

Know what works for you. Seek it with the intensity of shopping. It's there, and you can find it.

Emotion/Stress

When we get upset, we lose our sense of portion control. We lose sense of our ability to choose. We just want the emotional hurt to stop. We want the stress to go away. It's seldom that we are actually hungry. In fact, we may be feeling pretty full, but there is that memory of soothing when we put something in our mouths, and at that moment, that's pretty much all we can think about. Make it stop; just make it stop. Please make it stop.

Some of us had bad experiences in childhood, some really awful, and healing that is important. For many, it was less about abuse and more about the way we learned to deal with stress and our emotions, whether at two or 22. What we have used in the past has helped us, even as it hurts us in other ways. Some bite their nails or pull or twist their hair when they are anxious. Some burst with energy when staring down a deadline and do everything fast, and others slow down to a snail's pace. Some head to the snack machine, refrigerator, or pantry not sure what they want but rely on knowing something will do the trick. Isn't it interesting that it may not be a specific food but something in a general category that will soothe a particular emotion? It's almost opportunistic soothing rather than a specific remedy for an emotion that plagues us. Perhaps if we identified the true need, we wouldn't need edible soothing. That would stop us from grazing through several options on the way to that elusive soothing.

When my grandfather died, we sat around the kitchen table talking about the arrangements. I watched my mother move from the table to the stove to the cookie jar to the refrigerator and back to the table. A few minutes later, she made the circuit again. When she and I were alone at the table, and when she was about to get up again, I risked asking her if she was hungry or just needed something. We hugged it out, and she was okay. Still, when she passed away, I found myself doing the same thing until I remembered that conversation.

Food is easy comfort, and at some difficult times, it is abundantly available. Yet the relief is short-lived, momentary, and the feeling of loss repeats its request for comfort over and over because it's only soothed, not healed. This mechanism to try to cope with uncomfortable emotions or situations is comforting and works very well—even if only for a moment, and we'll take it. Healing seems impossible at that point.

We've managed our emotions okay this far, but our coping mechanism has created a new issue in our weight. Making a change to our coping strategy is hard, even frightening, and it takes time and effort to repeat it until it becomes the new way we handle our stress or other emotions.

We have to get to the place where sorting out the core issue is important enough to let go of the substitute. It does take time, and it's often fraught with more of a struggle, tears, and frustration than we expect. Like cleaning infection from a wound, it always gets worse before it gets better, but the better is significantly better. In the end, even if we find it hard to believe now, it's less work than struggling with whatever coping mechanism we've set up to support our old ways. It's a lot less expensive than pills and potions, clubs and monthly subscriptions to the next purported "This Will Melt the Fat Away with No Effort or Pain on Your Part" plans. Making the change requires some intention and commitment.

Facing our stuff means we'll be free from the compulsion to stuff our faces.

Imagine that.

Imagine what it might feel like to no longer need to put something in your mouth to feel better. Can you? Even for a moment, can you believe that's possible?

When that is true for us, there are no extra calories to counter later. There is no sluggish feeling because we just consumed three pieces of whatever sugar bomb we prefer. No down side, no awful feeling, no tangle of guilt. We simply find a moment of calm and settle there to get whatever it is we need. No food or beverage will ever bring as much peace, comfort, or calm as a moment of being free to make our own choices. That's true control.

And, yes, it is possible. There's no trick to it. It is a learned response, and it's not hard. It just takes a little bit of effort and choosing to do it differently.

Shifting Gears

I did some experimenting with what I actually liked and what I didn't. Tasting things isn't often part of the equation, is it? We just stuff it down and taste it later. When I stopped to focus on tasting some things, I realized I didn't really like them. It was astonishing. I'd eaten particular chocolates or brands for years.

I know that may be hard to believe. I could hardly believe it myself, but once I slowed down enough and savored the flavors, discerning between the combinations, it made a huge difference. Why had I continued to eat them and seemingly enjoy them? Maybe my palate matured when I wasn't looking. Whatever it was, it was a shock to suddenly realize what I had dreamed about, thought lovingly of, and overate was no longer something I wanted. That will save some calories, believe me.

Slowing down my eating made a significant difference. It's essential even if it is unfamiliar to most of us. As an experiment, time your next meal. How long does it take to complete a meal as you normally eat? Then consciously slow down, chew, put your fork down between bites, avoid washing your food down with a beverage, and see how long it takes to complete a meal.

Unless we're out for a formal dinner where everyone is applying their manners, I'm often the last one to finish. That wasn't always true. I inhaled my food along with the rest of my family. Then I recognized that it kept me from registering that I'd eaten, thus setting off the need for more. Once I slowed down to taste what I was eating and therefore to enjoy it, it took longer to consume, and it often meant I ate less and saved some calories. Bonus!

When we don't stop to taste things, we may as well eat cardboard. We don't really enjoy them when we swallow them whole, do we?

I addressed my own gluttonous habits. Seriously, taking a double portion of anything isn't good for me. I'm only five feet three inches tall. It doesn't take a lot of calories to maintain this frame, and some days it takes fewer calories than others. I learned to measure foods that were too easy to overeat. I learned to stop eating when I felt satisfied even if my plate wasn't yet clean—no more stuffing myself into a stupor. I had to recognize when I'm being silly or greedy. Yes, once in a while, some food will blow all good intentions. Once. In. A. While. Not every day or even every week. Moderation in all things.

I also plan for my needs around hunger. I know what meals stick with me and which ones might leave me hungry in a couple of hours. My responsibility as an adult is to take care of that, otherwise it's planned grumpiness. I carry a healthy snack, and skipping meals is no longer a diet strategy for me. I carry a measured portion of nuts with me or an ounce of cheese. It takes the edge off the hunger for me.

I worked with a friend and learned to work out a lot of issues I'd carried for years—old beliefs, habits, and thoughts that I'd clung to because they were familiar but didn't help me. At all. Once I settled some of the old issues, it freed me from anger, resentment, guilt, and shame for which I beat myself up, which only made me want to soothe myself with eating, and so went that unhelpful loop. Settling those issues gave me back an ability to choose for myself. Not for my family, not for what is expected of me, but simply what I might want or need. Without the negative thoughts repeating in my mind, I wasn't as negative. Without beating myself up, I felt better in general, less stressed and anxious.

Crazy isn't it? How we stress ourselves out when a couple of tweaks to our thinking and activity can free us. Crazier still how we tend to think that it is not possible.

For Your Consideration

One client said she sometimes struggled with gluttony:

It's such a nasty word, but I suspect it is more of a reality than many of us want to acknowledge, she said. I'm sure that eating a whole sleeve (or box) of Thin Mints is gluttony even if I try to convince myself I'm supporting a good organization.

What are the foods that catapult you into gluttony whether it's for a good cause or the average Saturday night?

What foods would you be willing to reconsider? You may have eaten them forever, but do you still like them?

What foods might be a good substitute for more calorie-laden choices?

What habits would you choose to reset?

CHAPTER FIVE

My Year Without Peanut Butter... and Other Addictive Cravings

Quick Start Guide: Things That Work

Some of us have bad experiences in our childhood that created our food issues. Whether abusive, offensive, sarcastic, or playful, we went to food for comfort. For others, it may be a good experience, a connection to someone or a time in our lives. When I catch a wafting scent of bread, I'm back in my grandmother's kitchen. Cinnamon, rosemary, and others put me in my mother's kitchen. Peanut butter connects me to all that was right with the world of my childhood. Instant comfort.

Foods that connect us to certain times, places, and people are powerful. If a particular food makes you stumble over and over, look for the association. If you find the association, you can regain control.

What makes that food work for you? When do you recall it first becoming important? What was going on in your life at the time? Is there a substitute or adjustment that would fill the nutritional need without kicking off your attachment to it? How can you meet the core need currently being filled by that food in a healthier way?

Or perhaps you don't see the association. Find a counselor or trusted friend to help you work through how that food draws you, calling your name again and again.

You know the one I mean. It's the food that calls to you not only when you are stressed but in any circumstance. You HAVE to have it. If you were asked to cut that food/drink from your diet, you might break out in a cold sweat or swear six ways to Sunday that you could not manage without it. Limiting consumption would be hard enough, but eliminating that food or beverage is out of the question. You just don't want to or simply won't. The facets of flavor or mouth-feel or whatever draws you to that food also supports and soothes you in any situation, and you just love it, lean on it, require it. THAT one.

Mine was peanut butter, which is a healthy protein source, but like many foods, eating too much of anything, even a good thing, leads to fat storage. I love the crunchy, natural version whose ingredients list only peanuts and a little salt to bring out their flavor. In my "fat free" days, I poured away the oil swimming on the surface before refrigerating. When I was stressed, bored, sad, mad, frustrated, lonely, annoyed, grieving, joyous, or be-bopping through my day, that wide-mouth jar called my name. The balance of salty, creamy, and crunchy had great mouth-feel, and the flavor was more-ish . . . as in drawing me to have even more. At 100 calories per tablespoon, prudence requires consumption in measured amounts. Sometimes I could, yet many times I could not.

I had two emotional connections to it, and when the connections severed, I had two very different reactions.

I learned to love peanut butter at the knees of both my grandmother and mother. An economical and easy protein source, even a half peanut butter sandwich easily kept me going for a good couple of hours. We loved it by the spoonful, a great snack—when you stop at one spoonful… and watch the size of that spoon, don't forget. If it was paired with chocolate, well, that was our definition of bliss.

When my mother passed away, I'd find myself at the refrigerator more often, spoon in hand and searching out the peanut butter. After my grandmother passed away, the frequency increased. When I realized what I was doing and began to see the results of over-consumption, I didn't give it up, but I tried to manage my portions and frequency. The taste was a connection to them somehow, and when I needed them, a little peanut butter would soothe that ache even if only a little.

Grief is a particularly revealing journey. We cannot walk around it but only through it. When we do try to walk around it, it tends to jump up and bite us later and in creative ways at the most awkward times. Food is a common thread of soothing during grief—either over-consumption or under-consumption depending on our coping mechanisms. Food is also a powerful memory trigger, and pairing that memory of food with the one we grieve makes a formidable connection.

My cousin was being transferred to an international assignment and could not take his dog with him, so Max, the 18-month-old Golden Retriever, came to live with us. There are some really intelligent dogs, but dear Max was not one of them. We decided he did have at least two working brain cells: Love me and Feed me. He so wanted to please and love us, and he was whole-hearted in his devotion to me. He became a precious companion over the 13 years we had together.

As noted previously, Max started my walking routine. He blew out an ACL, and part of the three-month rehab was a walk three times daily, starting at five minutes and working our way up to an hour, three times every day, rain or shine. Once his injury was rehabilitated, I was less consistent. Just over a year later, he blew out the other ACL, and we started the walking routine again. This time I was determined to maintain the practice for me as well as for him, and again, one walk once a day seemed easy, so we continued the morning constitutional.

He lived until just after his fifteenth birthday. As a senior gentleman, he'd had various medications through his later years, and particularly in his last year, we had a regular dose of medication served in peanut butter. He loved peanut butter as much as I did, and he'd take any medication if it had enough peanut butter to hide it in, so our morning ritual included peanut butter for him and some for me. Ellie, the puppy we'd added along the way, liked it, but she wasn't invested in it like Max and I were.

After Max died, I couldn't even look at the peanut butter jar without grieving. Ellie was a little disappointed, but I couldn't serve it. I could not have any kind of nuts quite honestly. I couldn't face the scent or the taste without tearing up. Perhaps it was the cumulative effect of loss of my peanut butter buddies or the tender place our pets occupy in our hearts, but it was a good six months before I could contemplate peanut butter and a year before it was back on my grocery list.

Our sense of taste and smell are powerful memory triggers, and I can't help but think of them even now. When thinking of my mom, my nan, and dear Max finally shifted from sorrow to a precious memory, I could enjoy it again. I consciously manage my portions or I could easily eat too much when I'm deep into my emotional stuff. Sometimes I just have to stop buying it to reinforce my control around consumption and my heart. It's how I manage myself, and that's okay. A jar of peanut butter no longer has to be in my pantry or refrigerator. I know where to get it, and I know which retailer will have my favorite brand when I'm feeling balanced again, and they'll keep it fresh and available for me until I'm ready. They even call it a "store."

Granted, that may sound blindingly obvious and perhaps a little flippant for a topic that is so hard to get around, and yet it's true.

Take a breath.

We're into some tough stuff in this chapter, so take a moment to settle and breathe. I know this is hard, and it stirs up our emotional stuff. It did for me.

I'd worked through a lot of stuff, and yet I still found myself at the refrigerator one day. I don't even remember what was going on, but something had wound me up, and I had to have peanut butter. I jerked open the door, pulled out my jar, and ripped away the brown and white checked lid. As it clattered onto the countertop, I'd picked up a spoon and quickly tossed it away. Fingers were faster.

As the scent wafted up to my nose, all the loss, all the frustration, the litany of "emotion de jour" I tangled with so often hit me. What I really wanted was my grandmother to tell me I was okay, that my value was not in my performance nor my shape, that my heart was true, helpful, and kind, and that I had value. I had value in being myself—my true self. I wanted to hear her say, "Just be my girl; I see your heart, and you don't need anything but to be yourself."

What I wanted was not in that jar. She was not in that jar, and neither was her encouragement. Peanut butter was a sweet connection, but it was not what I needed and would never be.

That was my moment. I screwed on the lid, put the jar back into the refrigerator, and I closed the door. I had to hold onto my value, to value my true self, and to affirm and encourage myself. Truth was not in my shape, not in what I looked like, not what I did. My value is in who I am.

Which ought to be blindingly obvious, but it isn't sometimes, is it? When we're deep in our stuff and struggling, that truth can easily be swept aside. The task is to choose to stop repeating the negative thoughts, arrest them, and flip them for our good. What we hear loud enough and long enough we begin to believe. Then we begin to repeat it about ourselves. Need we document any of those negative phrases you repeat to yourself? No, we know them all too well, and repetition of them will only reinforce them further—and who needs that?

Hang in there. Stay with me until you feel stronger. Breaking a lifetime's habit of going to food for what we need takes time and intention, but it can be done when we marshal all our courage and conviction into motivation. You can do this.

How does any food occupy such a place in our lives? How do our emotions get so entangled between our relationships and a specific food? More to the point, how do we escape that emotional trap of trying to let food meet an emotional need? It makes no logical sense, does it? Yet the entanglement is real to us.

In the cold light of the refrigerator, we may falter, giving it far too much power to adjust our moods, and then we believe we can do nothing about it. If someone tried to tell us that we could take control, we'd dismiss them. Yeah right, you don't understand. You don't know. You've never experienced what I'm experiencing, so just go away and leave me alone with my nachos, chocolate, or cheesecake. I can't get through this experience without _____.

I know. It feels that way. It's the way we've done the best we could in the situation at hand, and it has worked for us on that front. Or we eat (or drink) at night because of XYZ. We're tired. We've used up all our limited resource of willpower for the day, and we just need it.

For all that pushback, take a moment to honestly consider the remote, potential, far-fetched, unlikely, theoretical if distant possibility of perhaps having the tools to relate to this food differently if you so choose. Briefly. You can always dismiss what you find, and the strength of resistance could be a signal of the strength of that attachment. Do you want to be free of that hold it has on you? Do you want to feel in control of your choices?

When we look outside ourselves for something to fill a space in our hearts, it never truly works, and the space comes back, usually bigger and more demanding the next time. It's like a cheap, flimsy adhesive bandage. As long as there is no exterior stress, as long as it doesn't get wet, it will protect the wound. Once it's wet, it falls off, leaving the wound exposed and vulnerable.

Our comfort foods are just as flimsy. They work while the flavor lingers in our mouths, but when that sense dissipates, so does the comfort, leaving the wound again exposed and vulnerable. We will try more expensive bandages, stronger adhesives, or re-wrap our wounds. The wound is never healed by the bandage. In fact, covering some wounds prevents their healing.

Some wounds heal on their own. Some require a little help, and some require that someone who knows more about them help to heal them. When a wound gets infected, a bandage may only make it worse. If it festers, the infection can spread and require even more care than if it had been properly cared for in the beginning.

Our emotional wounds require similar care. Some can resolve on their own or within a short time of care, perhaps covering them to prevent infection. When the wound doesn't heal, we can continue to reapply a bandage, but we know how that works out, don't we? Infected emotional wounds require significant intervention.

The prevalence of addiction in our culture is indicative of our search, and some of us have chosen more socially acceptable substances, but each one ravages us all the same. It's still a dependence on something outside ourselves to make us feel better rather than finding that comfort within ourselves. Like the pacifier of infancy, we hold onto that food instead of finding a healthier and more effective away to soothe ourselves.

How do we change that?

As always, the first step is recognizing what we're doing and being honest about our individual needs, desires, and thresholds of temptation. A good indicator of being "hooked" is that sense of panic when someone suggests removing it from your life and shopping list. Could you do without it? Can it be available in your pantry or refrigerator? Can it be open or in plain sight? What pushes you over the edge of temptation?

When I lived in the UK, peanut butter was not available. I missed it, but I wasn't as aware of the attachment, and I was off on an adventure with many new foods, customs, and people to distract me from old habits and choices. Once I returned, all of my desire for missed foods, friends and family, and experiences were magnified along with things, people, and experiences I missed from Wales but could not easily have in the States. There were months when I couldn't have peanut butter in the house because in a weak moment all my resolve dissolved, and I ate too much. My willpower was not strong enough to overcome my perceived need. Rather than test myself, it was easier to abstain. Everyone is different, so recognize your limits, and then do what you need to do to support your goal.

Then dig deep to identify what the food is doing for you. What do you need when you substitute this food in its place? What's the feeling you're seeking? Comfort from what? Or from whom?

"When I go to this food/beverage, what I want (or don't want) is _____."

Whatever the answer, stay with it. Feel it, feel its absence or presence. Don't run from it, try to cover it, or dismiss it—that feeling will just chase you down. It's true for you, and that's okay. Feel it. Let it wash over you like a wave. It may dissipate, or a bigger wave may follow, but stay with it and let it wear itself out. What we fear will happen when we face the scary interior of our hearts and minds is often worse than the reality. Like a monster in the darkness of our childhood bedroom, when we turn on the light, it will dissipate.

We know what we go to the food for, what we want, but what does it *actually* do for us? Momentary calm maybe, but then what? Sometimes it's a romanticized idea of what the food does for us. For me, the excessive portions of peanut butter added pounds. That was the reality. "Once over the lips, forever on the hips." It didn't bring back the relationships. It didn't even begin to take the place of being with my missing family. It just made me feel fat.

It's not the food, it's what the food does for us—the comfort, the love, the respite, the memory, the perceived solution to the loneliness or loss. Identify what it does, and find another way to soothe that. What does your heart need? Can you find that within yourself? Can you self-soothe? If you don't feel you can right now, is there a healthier substitution? Go back to your list from Chapter Two: What do you need? A walk, something calming? Ten minutes of something that makes you giggle? When that food calls your name, what from that list would do a better job of filling that space?

For now, if you need a healthier crutch, allow it to support you as you work to strengthen yourself until you can find what you need within you to provide the soothing. You have it already, but you aren't yet convinced that you do. That's okay for now—as long as you're working to gain the strength you need.

If you stumble, pick yourself up again and keep walking. You did it the other way for years, so an automatic response of going to that food is part of the process. Diligence is your friend here. As you continue to choose the actions that support your goal more often than you work on autopilot, you'll find your goal growing nearer and nearer. Keep choosing for your best.

You can be honest with yourself. Often we don't want growth and change; we simply want a different result. Growth would require us to do things differently, to change our habits and food patterns. Dang it.

The truth is that most of the time we'd prefer to swallow a pill that magically allows us to eat whatever and however much we want without putting on any weight. That's the result we want! Of course we do. How many diet pills—pardon me, nutritional supplements—have you purchased believing they would make the weight fall off?

Yeah, me too, back in the day. What we likely need is to manage our nutrition differently. Eat according to our actual physical hunger rather than our emotional demands. Find what we actually need and get that in some way rather than stuffing our feelings and needs.

When you overindulge, what is it that you really want? Often when we want something to last, we have to grow into that change or make adjustments to support it as we grow. Growing pains and practicing new behaviors can feel harder in the midst of it, and yet those kinds of changes can last. Be of good courage and soldier on, and be kind to yourself.

Shifting Gears

It helped me to get real clear about what I wanted. My ultimate goal was to get down to a certain weight and size. I had this pair of jeans I'd been able to wear for about five minutes 20 years before, and that served as my visual for the goal. To get there, I had to consistently make good choices over several months.

For a time, that meant not buying certain foods or having them in the house, which was sad by itself. I worked through the exercise of facing the emotion. Anticipating facing that emotion was worse than doing it. Our imaginations are great at creating the worst possible scenario, aren't they? Not that the experience wasn't tough, but letting the emotion crest was surprising. The sadness didn't drown me. It fell away. It didn't last as long as I thought it would, and once it had passed, it was over for that time. Simply over. No lingering moodiness.

The process actually took less time than going to find the food, and it didn't require a second or third helping to manage it. The emotional crisis was simply done—a little muss and fuss but then the feeling passed. The next time the emotion threatened, I let it come, and again, it crested and fell away. If that was as bad as feeling this emotion was going to be, that wasn't nearly as scary as I imagined. Funny thing was that the feeling didn't raise its ugly head as often either.

Once it passed, I didn't need anything else. I could return to whatever I was doing with no lingering negative thoughts or feelings. The negative power of the emotion dissipated. Not that I forgot it, but the wound healed, and anytime the old emotion flickered, it worked as a kind of signal for me that I was neglecting my self-care. I'd consult my heart and find what it needed, and there was no longer a need for the ineffective old way of coping.

For Your Consideration

What food calls your name?

If you eliminated that food from your shopping list, would another take its place?

If so, we must disarm that trigger for comfort eating.

45-second trigger disarm protocol:
Breathe.
What are you feeling?
What do you need—not the food, the need?
How can you meet that need right now?
Will you choose to allow that to soothe you?
Breathe and let it be.

The only magic bullet for weight loss is the power of your intention.

CHAPTER SIX

Break That Blinkin' Yo-Yo

Quick Start Guide: Things That Work

We see the perfect body splashed across magazines, television, and film. We also recognize that the bodies are often edited to that perfection, and yet it doesn't change our wish to achieve such, does it? Fairy Godmothers on call for anyone?

We're pretty certain of what we don't want. I bet you can call up a seriously clear and vivid image of that. Perhaps that's the way you see your body even now whether or not it's true from anyone else's perspective.

Funny how my image of what I do want is less vivid. I can cut pictures from a magazine to create the arms, legs, hips, and torso I'd like, and yet I still can't quite picture my head on that body.

What is the perfect body for you? What will it look like when you reach your goal weight? It helps to have a mental image to work toward. Ever tried to put together a jigsaw puzzle without benefit of the picture from which it comes? It's hard to find something when we don't know what it looks like.

Now, we have to be sensible with this part. I'll never stretch from five foot three to even five foot five, so there's no way I'll be statuesque. EVER. In an honest assessment of what is possible given your genes and potential, what's the best version of the body you have? Perhaps you've been there before and can remember. Or maybe you have an outfit you used to wear that can be the vision of your goal. If you have that outfit, hang it where you can see it. Allow it to motivate and keep you on track. And I do mean motivate rather than mock. In the midst of working toward a goal, we sometimes get on the dark side of our thinking which is part of what got us to where we are. Choose the more positive track, and it will serve you well.

What diet is your favorite yo-yo?

Toy yo-yos were invented in ancient Greece, and they make an appearance in schools now and again. Brightly colored plastic disks with string made a great playground game that increased fine motor skills and eye-hand coordination long before computer games. One can quickly rise to King/Queen of the Playground when he or she gets good enough to advance beyond the simple tricks like "The Sleeper" and "Walk the Dog."

The cyclical rising and falling mechanism gave us one of our best known terms for the dieting conundrum: The Yo-Yo diet.

Ah, we know it well.

It's that crash diet we try when we can't fit into our outfit for a special occasion. We need to lose those 10 pounds fast! So we starve ourselves, try a liquid diet, eat odd food combinations, or choose the latest pill that will "melt the fat right off us." If motivated enough, we can manage that just long enough to get through the event.

Great! We've lost those pounds, then once the event is over, all our hunger storms back in. Without the motivating shame and guilt about how we look being on display for people we haven't seen for some time and probably won't see again for a long time, our drive dissipates, and we believe we can no longer control ourselves, and why should we have to? All our good intentions of maintaining the loss evaporate at sight of that huge bagel with extra cream cheese and jam, at the all-you-can-eat buffet (you've paid for it, right?), at that happy hour with meal-sized snacks, at a holiday table, or at the fast food order window, and quickly we've regained that number of pounds, and they brought a few pesky friends along with them! We heave a big sigh of frustration and anger at ourselves when we hit the scales or try to button that waistband.

If we have grown wise to this phenomenon, perhaps we worked a more sensible plan over time to dispatch that excess weight in good time for the event. Once past the event, at first we are very pleased with our work, and we do make better choices at least half the time, and we are able to manage our choices for a while. Then life sort of happens, and maybe a little extra nibble here or an indulgence there gives way to another little cheat here and another one there. It's my birthday or my friend's birthday. They brought cake or pizza to the office. We're on vacation, and calories don't count on vacation, right? Everyone else is having _____, so why shouldn't I get to join in? It would be rude to decline!

It doesn't happen overnight, but by the next New Year's Eve, weight loss of a good 10 to 20 pounds—or more—again hits your list of resolutions. It's normal. It's natural. It happens. Most of the celebrities who endorse the national programs fall prey to this, so why not me? Or we think this is just how dieting works—lose 20 regain 15, lose those 15, gain 25, lose five, gain five, or the insidious lose three, gain three that shifts into lose four, gain six, keeping us further and further from the weight we claim as our goal. We might quickly find ourselves on a constant diet (when we stick to it), and we yo-yo on the scales year round.

Welcome to "The Sleeper" yo-yo diet. We are just spinning at the end of the string, waiting for the next trick that promises to fix our weight with some magical method. Or we've fallen asleep to our choices, habits, or desires for a healthier lifestyle, and here we are again trying on a bigger size or being unhappy with the way our current size fits. Big sigh.

Ready for an exit strategy?

Recognize the Issue

There is no exit without acknowledging the issue. I know that disgust with self and the process, and I know that hope against all sense and experience for this miracle cure to actually produce the results. We want a QUICK exit that works, the kind of instant gratification that we long and look for in everything else. Instant pudding, instant relief, instant success, instant everything—and the results are always just as good as the version that takes time to create, right? Sure! Then we can stay with it, motivated by the results, right? It will be easy once we make it to our goal, won't it?

Until we get really hungry for whatever reason, and that sets off a binge. One binge often leads to a little indulgence here, a slip there, and another there, and before we know it . . .

A quick exit leads to an equally quick return to pattern because we didn't break it at all. We may have bent it a little, but we didn't break our pattern. Ask any of the gastric surgery patients who five years later have returned to their original weight, or heavier. They may have had themselves physically altered, but they never broke their food and emotional patterns, and therefore the impulses to eat to excess returned over time.

Breaking it is key. We have to be willing to break our usual pattern of choices and not step back into them. It's as essential as changing our route when we move from one home to another. We don't return to the old house, do we? No, we drive to our new place, park in that garage, live in that floor plan, plant that flower garden—live in the space we now occupy rather than returning to the habits and choices that created the girth we say we no longer want.

That doesn't mean never having what we want again.

It does mean being responsible with when, where, and how we have what we want.

We do this with our financial budgets.

We do this with our taxes.

We do this with our time and family life.

And because we're so responsible in other areas, sometimes we think food is a place to cut loose. It's a little everyday kind of luxury. Food becomes the one soother we can hold onto. It's not illegal or unethical, and it's a safe indulgence, right? Or if we just combine these specific foods in this way—or never eat THAT food again—or take in more of this, we'll find the key to the fat just falling off us.

Spinning at the end of the string again?

Insidious, isn't it?

The cycle begins when we let go of the nutritional pattern that may have been limited but worked and relax back into our old way of eating and exercising or not. When we go back to the way we always ate before, we'll get the results we always do. There is no way around that. Our bodies can only use so many calories, carbohydrates, proteins, and fats (pick your diet philosophy) before it shifts into fat storing mode. Magic wands aside, of course.

Find Your Sweet Spot

Once our "diet" is over and we arrive at the weight, size, and measurements we want, nutrition is still key. We know what nutritional patterns increase the numbers and what patterns decrease them. Making some of the changes a permanent part of our lives helps to maintain the bodies we claim we want. Whether the change is in volume or components, it is essential to focus on how foods affect our bodies.

It's so tempting once we're released from the rigors of a "diet" to splurge with reckless abandon on all the things we didn't allow ourselves to have while we were controlling our consumption.

You can have them all, a little at a time.

Patience. If you were losing about a pound a week, you likely cut your caloric intake vs. expenditure by 500 calories a day, or 3,500 calories per week. Add that back in gently, increasing your calories to the rate of expenditure. Try adding one or two foods each week to see how it affects you, and adjust as needed to stop the loss or gain. Finding your optimal fuel mix takes a little time and focus, but the result can mean you'll never have to "diet" again. Just imagine what that would be like! Like sticking to a budget, saving for a rainy day, or doing an annual check-up—the preventative maintenance, self-care, and control maintains the balance with minimal effort. And you won't have to reschedule any doctor appointments because you really want to lose a couple of pounds first.

Yes, me too, in the old days.

Still want to splurge? Okay. That is human, but try to be wise about it. Start with identifying what that desire to splurge is about. Is it the relief from having to focus so much on what you were eating? The joy of freedom? A reward for diligence? Making up for lost time? What drives that desire to eat with reckless abandon? Finding the source of that desire can help to disarm that trigger.

If you decide to have whatever it is, then simply plan for the intake. Measure the portion, shuffle a few calories later, and make room in your nutrition plan for that splurge. Honor your experience of consuming this food or drink with the same measure you're giving your desire. Set an elegant table, using proper utensils, plate, and glass. Sit down and enjoy what you're eating. Sometimes if we take the time to enjoy it, we can be satisfied with two or three bites of something we love and therefore we don't have to over-indulge.

Michael always chooses a dessert accounting for giving me two or three bites of it. He's kind and generous that way. He knows I hate to waste food, so I'll either not take a serving and miss it, or I'll take the serving and regret it. So, he sets aside three French fries for me, a taste of his cake—or even the whole portion of the frosting, which is the part I like best, a sip of some drink. If I've planned ahead, I may have a serving, but sometimes all I really want is a taste. It works for us. How can you and your partner or a friend support and encourage each other in meaningful ways? Work out your system and use it to motivate, encourage, and support your goals.

Set an Internal Alarm

Set an alarm in your mind. There are weeks that I don't actually need my alarm clock, when I turn it off before it rings. Then there are days or weeks when I depend on that alarm to wake me up to avoid oversleeping. I might snooze it once, but that means working harder to get out the door on time which defeats the purpose of the extra nine minutes of sleep.

Look around. The United States has increased in girth. Over a third of Americans are obese. That's not just overweight—that's a body mass index of 30 or more. As a nation, we are basically intelligent, industrious people, but we are asleep on this issue.

Following the attacks of September 11, 2001, the airlines were hurting, and they looked for ways to decrease costs. They floated an idea out to the general public to charge fees according to a passenger's weight as planes require more fuel to transport heavier loads. It was immediately shot down as rude, offensive, insensitive, and cruel. Opposition said we could not weigh a woman in public as they already have body issues. Imagine the vulnerable teenage girl already struggling—or the gangly teenage boy who hadn't yet hit his growth spurt and barely hits 110 pounds. That idea went away quickly, and they reduced the number and weight of bags we could carry instead. When insurance companies and the government health care debate considered adding fees for overweight or obese employees' costs, the practice was again shot down as insensitive, harsh, and unfair.

As a culture, we have simply accepted that our body sizes have increased with all the attendant limitations and complications affecting everyone, and being heavier is generally accepted, apart from the catty realm of conversation.

We may not get a national alarm, but we can set our personal alarm. Our weight varies from day to day by a pound or two, and an indulgent weekend can create a bump in weight, so give yourself some grace. Weigh as often as you feel comfortable to do so. We all get lax or obsessive about certain issues, so do what works for you. If the two-pound fluctuation will send you into a tailspin, don't weigh daily. If you know your weight creeps but you don't weigh to avoid the evidence, then you might want keep closer tabs on the scale.

Make note of an upper limit that is acceptable to you, and I'd suggest a couple of pounds over that daily variation rate rather than waiting for it to increase to more than five pounds. When you hit that upper limit, make changes that day rather than waiting until Monday or whatever day of the week you choose. Don't snooze it too often or it will get out of hand before you realize. Correcting our course quickly will save a significant effort of having too many pounds to lose. And who wants to do that again?

Know Your Accountability Style

I've known people who could set a goal, work at it, and attain it without any outside encouragement or affirmation. That's fantastic, and it's not me. Some need a group to keep them motivated, but one person, maybe two, checking in with me now and again helps me stay on track. Others either don't need or don't want outside accountability. We're all different in what fills our needs for staying on track to meet goals.

The pressure to approach your goal just like your friends approach theirs can be overwhelming, but recognize what you need is essential for your success and therefore equally valid. Your style may require a bit more or a bit less work, but you can set up the support structure you need to get you firmly into an eating and exercise pattern. Build in a few spot checks along the way even when you feel you won't need them. If you don't actually need them, allow it to be an affirmation of your work. If you do need a little kick, it's already set up.

Be Vigilant, Patient, and Kind

A day of detouring from our plan now and again is fine. A week and a half is not. Some of us figure it out and can stay within our parameters forever, and some of us may have to work at this. Forever.

Others may choose to let it go and be okay with the result. That's still an option. No one (currently) can make us monitor our weight and fitness, and we can simply buy bigger sizes and celebrate the body we have. There may be consequences of health, mobility, etc., but those can be planned around much more easily in our current culture of acceptance. Be kind to yourself.

If you choose to continue with vigilance, when your alarm goes off, attend to it immediately. However, we must be patient with ourselves as well as kind, recognizing we are still frail creatures of dust. We can't get it right every day in every situation, but if we check in with our hearts to see how the situation got out of hand, we can get it right more often.

What's going on when we detour? Are we neglecting our hearts? Is there a situation at work or home that we're avoiding dealing with or that we cannot affect? What's going on in our environment that pushes our buttons? Is it a planned detour? Or did something knock us off our center? The only way to break a habit is to look at it, evaluate what works or doesn't, and choosing to make choices differently for as long as it takes to make the new behavior habitual.

The Fallback Plan

What is the bare minimum you could do to stay on track today? Mini habits can be your friend. What's the smallest step you can take toward your goal in this moment? Often we think, "Well, I've blown it for today," and then we go to an extreme. Either we throw off all controls and blow out all our calories for the week in one sitting, or we decide fasting for the rest of the day or maybe the week is in order. Sleeping at the end of the string again, aren't we?

Take one step toward your goal. Drink more water, have extra vegetables, throw out the food you can't control yet, go for a walk, play with your kids, measure your portions. Find a way to regain your footing and then hold on until the crisis passes. Start again, and keep starting again. You only fail when you give up altogether unless you choose to forget about it and settle yourself with the results.

Look for ways you may be sabotaging yourself. The yo-yo tends to burn away muscle on the way down and adds fat on the return. That reduces the metabolic rate and increases fat storage, and we want that metabolic rate to burn at optimum. What patterns do you see? Are there ways you can counter your usual pattern? One of my "fixes" is to keep foods I monitor in the freezer. It's out of sight, and although leftover cake with butter cream frosting does taste pretty good even frozen, I'm less likely to indulge on a whim if it's not as easily accessible. Check your patterns for sabotage and rework them.

Look after your needs. The brain needs food to control impulses, so to lose effectively, you do have to eat. Fasting—while a useful practice for health, focus, and clarity—isn't the most efficient strategy for weight loss unless one is well-able to control one's mind and impulses. Reducing calories to below the minimum daily requirement tends to slow metabolism as part of the body's survival instinct. So, no skipping—unless you're referring to the play (and exercise) we enjoyed as children. Skipping meals often has a boomerang effect that leads to desperate overeating.

Pay attention to alcohol intake. Note I'm not advocating abstinence. It's another category of calories to monitor, and if you're so inclined to partake, then pay attention to the calorie counts. Some say alcohol reduces our store of Leptin, the hormone that signals satiety. Others say it reduces the body's efficiency for burning calories. It can lessen our sense of portion size and resolve, and that can be plenty of disruption. Pay attention.

Remember: It's often the satisfaction, the self-medication you're looking for—not the food.

Shifting Gears

My personal alarm is between three and five pounds. Maybe I've had too many events running close together or maybe it was a holiday or a brain blip kind of lack of awareness. Weight varies day to day, but my waistband never lies. I know how my trousers and skirts fit. When the scale sticks at this range longer than I want, that's my signal to wake up and pay attention for a couple of days or weeks.

Sometimes all it requires is a simple awareness of what I'm eating or not eating, how I'm working out or skipping it too often, or not taking in enough water. My mother used to say new pounds are more mobile. They don't stick around as long if you get on them right away.

That alarm is a wakeup call for me to pay attention. Check the labels if I've tried new foods, looking for nutrient numbers as well as portion sizes. Be more diligent about getting in my full round of exercise. Drink more water. Have I wandered back to the peanut butter too often? Am I consuming trigger foods? And, if so, what's going on? What do I need to alter in my heart and kitchen? It's time to focus on what works for me.

For Your Consideration

What's your yo-yo diet?

How does weighing in affect you?

Break down your patterns. What nutritional patterns work for you? How do you get off your pattern? Do certain foods affect you? How can you manage them more effectively for your goals?

What is your accountability style, and how can you utilize it to help you reach your goals?

Do you want to lose the weight? Are you willing to do what it takes to get there? Or would you truly prefer to stay where you are and celebrate all of you?

We stuff down our feelings and follow it with a food chaser.

CHAPTER SEVEN

Learn the Lesson, Drop the Guilt

Quick Start Guide: Things That Work

Ralph Waldo Emerson said, "The reward of a thing done well is to have done it."

Once you get to your chosen weight or size, enjoy it. Revel in the fact that you have done this task well. Your body is your reward, buying new clothes is a reward, feeling really good about the way you look and how your clothes fit are fantastic rewards. How can you value that reward more than that double chocolate cake with ice cream, whipped cream, nuts, and a cherry that will leave you feeling awful later? When you feel a little sick from over-indulging, will you still feel you have done the task well?

If so, go have it. You may need to simply enjoy it. Or it may vividly remind you of why you don't have a whole one to yourself anymore.

The twin buddies of guilt and shame can be immobilizing and self-defeating. They achieve a result, often at the hand of another person, but I can certainly heap my own brand of guilt and shame onto myself to great effect. Guilt is an effective persuasion technique, and it can serve for our good. We feel guilty for something we have done or didn't do. Afterward, we can try to make it right, learn from it, and go on. Hopefully.

On its less helpful side, we may get caught up in guilt, using it as a stick to beat up ourselves rather than utilizing the motivation to doing things differently. That's a corruption of guilt and the lesson it can teach us. When guilt comes at the hand of another, it may "help" us do what we know to be the right thing, or we may feel resentment and resistance to doing what the other wants. That can be as simplistic as a clash of personal preferences, as predictable as teenage rebellion, or just sheer orneriness to protect against what we feel is an intrusion. Whatever the circumstance and who's involved, guilt can motivate us to improve or damage our growth and progress.

Shame is feeling bad about who we are, about any or all the unique qualities, talents, preferences, and components that make us individuals. Something about us just isn't good enough, whether or not we can name the specifics. It's just awful us. Perhaps the shame begins with feeling guilt over a behavior whether or not we were yet old enough to know it was wrong or whether we were still learning right from wrong. Perhaps shame comes from a choice or a mistake we've made. At its best, the bad feeling is an inner control mechanism to guide us away from behaviors that do not serve us or those around us. However, we have then translated that as an indictment of who we are and buried ourselves under all kinds of stuff—habits, new choices, idiosyncrasies, coping mechanisms, addictions—and thought that was how to manage our awful selves.

Like guilt, shame sometimes comes at the hand of another and may well serve to control behavior, although through humiliation. Even when well-intentioned, shaming can be damaging in addition to being effective. When it begins a pattern, it can intertwine with guilt and bite us over and over and over. That's a powerful component in addiction, tamping down the guilt or shame with our comfort food or drink or other forms of self-medication.

For the purposes of growth, any learning tool that doesn't spur positive action is not helpful. Generations of parents would likely wish they had a way to predict the future so they'd know when their teaching efforts would spur the positive and when it would spur destruction. Bless them. They were doing the best they could.

Yet we use guilt and shame on ourselves, don't we? Some of us believe we are broken, damaged beyond redemption if others REALLY knew us, knew the actions we feel guilty about or the parts of which we are ashamed. Or we feed the cycle, feel fat and guilty, grow ashamed, then stuff ourselves with comfort foods to make us feel better, which makes us feel fat and guilty, grow ashamed, then stuff ourselves, rinse, repeat, ad nauseam.

With my clients, my first job is to excavate. We gently brush away all the years of collected dust, dig down through the clutter of the woulda coulda shouldas, unwrap the chains that bind, and extract the expectations of and performance for others. We collect the artifacts and treasures that we may not fully recognize or simply dismiss. Patiently we work through the muck toward finding their true hearts, the ones so buried by guilt and shame that they've forgotten who they really are. Once we clear all that stuff away, we can again stand, shake off the dust, and walk freely again in our true selves.

If you believed you were free, unencumbered by the past, family history, mistakes, and poor choices; if you believed you were as you were meant to be, not damaged or broken in any way; if you could instantly transport your best self into a new dimension, taking all the good with you; what would you do differently? Change? Become?

If I could assign a task to make this possible, would you do it? Accept it as true?

Exercise

List all the things you feel guilty about or shame over.

Go on, just let it rip. Do it on a separate sheet of paper if you want to keep it more hidden, but make a list. Everything. Justify why you're such an awful human being—from the mistakes to the intentional acts that didn't work out as you hoped. From buying the newest triple-decker snow cone on offer for yourself and leaving your brother without money to buy even a single when you were nine to whatever you did yesterday to maintain your guilt and shame level. You can list being born if you feel that's true. There's no hook on the next page to say you have to go share this with anyone—in fact, you can burn the page afterward if you like—but just be honest with yourself about what you've done or been that is so blinking awful. Whether it's true or not, whether you want anyone else to know or not, whether someone else told you or you decided for yourself, list the guilt and shame you've carried for 20 to 60 years or even for a minute and a half. Make columns if you wish: True or False Belief, Someone Told Me or I Chose This, Distant Past or Recent, Adult or Child. Make it work for you.

Need an example? Okay, I'll go first.

One of the things about me that I tried for years to conquer was biting my nails. Disgusting habit that I vowed to conquer almost as often as I resolved to lose weight. I tried everything—the stuff that tastes bad, nail polish, barriers like gloves, getting a manicure as well as counseling—and I'd do well for a while, but I'd always return to the habit. I even had fake nails. My manicurist could not believe anyone could bite their way through acrylic nails. In my counseling practice, I've even helped others eliminate the habit, but I struggled with it for years, and it was shameful for me, but not quite shameful enough to accomplish kicking the habit. In talking with a colleague, we talked about when the habit began, and I realized it started when I was in kindergarten.

My report card came in a manila envelope with our initials in the top right hand corner. I was five, and I'd learned how to write my initials, so I decorated the rest of the front of my envelope with my initials. I was quite pleased as I carefully wrote out each initial in as perfect form as I could manage using a big black magic marker. I was so proud.

My mother and father were not so proud. In fact, they were quite angry, and they kept going on about defacing school property. I didn't quite understand their reaction. Didn't they see how well I'd made my letters? How clever and creative I was to decorate my envelope?

The only thing I did understand was that something about me was awful. I didn't really understand why, but my actions, my impulse, my creativity, my skills created one little mess of a redhead who was just awful. Yes, five and six year olds can be overly dramatic.

I was so ashamed that I hid my report card in my coat as I rode in the carpool to school the next morning. When I timidly gave it to my teacher, her jaw dropped, and I knew I had so disappointed Mrs. Thompson. I was mortified. That was reinforced every six weeks as I was given the "soiled" envelope again and again.

Curiously, I started biting my nails, my handwriting grew smaller, and I buried my creativity under a pile of shame.

What I made of that experience was not their intention for me. They wanted to impress upon me the importance of respecting school property, which is an important lesson. Some of the lessons I took from that experience were valid. Other lessons were not, and they had a significant impact on my feelings of guilt and shame that only gathered more evidence as I grew and worked my way through life and school. I was never again frivolous with school property, and my respect for following rules was a bit rigid, perhaps too rigid, but I knew that if I followed rules, there would be less to feel guilty about or ashamed of.

Looking back at that experience as an adult, I can see the intended lesson. The anxiety I felt dissipated, and my nail biting diminished. I could also release that shame and reclaim my joy in creativity. My handwriting is still a work in progress.

Over to you. Did you do yours? If not, do it now.

Done? Good, let's analyze it. Look at each entry, column, and designation. Now that it's on paper, it may be easier to handle. If not, hang in there. We're not beating ourselves. We're simply observing and evaluating what we have believed up to now. Be kind to yourself. It's a learning process.

1. Is it valid?

In the cold light of adulthood, is there anything on that list that isn't true? Anything that wasn't deserved? Inaccurate? Were you falsely accused? Did we have the capacity to know it was right or wrong? Read that as whether or not it was age-appropriate at the time rather than whether or not it was an authority figure's desire for me to know by then. Evaluate the list for validity. It's okay to take the stance of an objective, wise, and kind mentor who considers the motive, capabilities, and intentions at the time.

2. Is it mine?

Does this moment of guilt or shame actually belong to me? Is it something I did/chose? Or was it someone else's action/preferences? Did their preferences or actions fit me? Might they have been projecting their own fears/guilt/shame/choices on me and reacting to that rather than what I did or how I reacted? Look at my boundaries in this situation.

If the incident truly has nothing to do with me, I won't hold onto it. That would be a very unfortunate case of stealing, and I'm not a thief of the consequences of someone else's expectations or actions.

3. What did I learn?

Did this experience of shame or guilt teach me something I still utilize? In a good way? Or less helpful?

What triggers has this experience set? How can I recognize and disarm them?

How have I chosen differently? Good or less helpful?

How has that experience helped me as I've grown and matured? What has it helped me to do or stopped me from doing that has been beneficial?

If I haven't learned from it yet, what can I learn now? How do I turn this experience toward my good?

4. What do I need to forgive?

In myself and others?

Forgiveness can be the magic wand of long-term change. I'm not kidding. Granted, it's hard. I know it's hard. I was born a natural redhead, and stubbornness was not just a cliché for me.

Forgiveness is a choice, and we make that choice until it no longer presents itself. You've seen the quotes. So many have been used so much that we're not sure of the origin anymore. I have an entire file dedicated to forgiveness because it's been too much of a challenge for my heart.

"Forgiveness doesn't excuse their behavior. Forgiveness prevents their behavior from destroying your heart."

"To forgive is to set a prisoner free and realize the prisoner was you."

"When you forgive, you in no way change the past, but you do change the future."

One of my favorite quotes in the autumn is, *"The trees are about to show us how lovely it can be to let dead things go."*

Forgiving doesn't feel quite right—until it does. It's like carrying a load with my hands full. I can't take hold of the good until I put something down. Once I put down something I no longer want, I have a hand to take hold of what I do want. It's hard, but it's well worth the effort. Once I've chosen to forgive myself and others— note, forgiving self is equally important—then I begin to act like I've forgiven them and myself. It may take some time, but when I keep choosing to forgive, I will be acting in a forgiving way, and that will create the feeling of forgiveness.

When the old thought comes up (and it will for a while), I choose forgiveness. I say to myself, "No, I don't want to think that way anymore. I'm choosing more helpful thoughts for the purpose of freeing myself.

5. What positive action resulted from this guilt or shame?

What did I learn? How have I done things differently as a result of this experience? How do I do this differently next time? What do I need to just let go of and leave in the past? What from this experience motivates me to be my best?

6. What can I do about this issue now?

Is there anything I can do to change the situation? What can I do to change the effect of it on myself or others? Is there anything I can do? If so, how do I do it? If I truly cannot do anything about this issue, how do I release it? Transfer it to someone who can? Make amends? Seek forgiveness? Make peace with the results or others involved?

7. How can I create a positive action/reaction/choice from this guilt or shame?

With what I've learned (or let go of), what do I do from here?

8. How do I affirm myself to help me release this guilt/shame?

Okay, full disclosure, for a long time I blew off affirmations. They seem so corny, and some can be, *and* they're more effective at getting us where we want to be than the negations we allow to run without question or censure. If all that negative self-talk has been so effective at keeping us stuck in our comfort eating and other issues, refilling our mental tank with positive statements could launch us to amazing heights. The key is to find the ones that work for us.

Think of it like doing mental weight lifting. When we start lifting weights, it seems a bit silly when they hand us three-pound dumbbells. It's not really enough, but it trains our muscles into the most effective form. Then we add weight, and we notice the soreness the next morning. Strength does not come to us without soreness and muscle cramps. We can't see the toning of our muscles, but one day we recognize bags are not as heavy as they once were, and we can do more than we used to be able to do. Bear the simple weight of the corny affirmations, and then move on to some that are more challenging and meaningful to you. Collect a few that challenge your heart or that you want to be true even if they aren't true yet. We can grow into them.

9. Make peace.

Make peace with others if you caused some kind of offense, and seek peace with those who have offended you. Apologize if needed, make amends if you can. If peace is needed in your own heart, make peace with the issue. There is grace, and all we need to do is accept it. Holding onto offense only gives us a frown, wrinkles, and gray hair. Go to a shopping area and watch people pass by. Look for those who have a peaceful countenance. Compare them to those who are angry, bitter, and agitated. Which would you prefer to emulate?

10. Practice.

When we've done it another way for a long, long time, we may need some time to practice doing things differently. When you catch yourself in the midst of an old behavior or thought, note it, and choose to do it differently. No need for beating ourselves up for the diversion. We're learning. We recognized it this time, and now we can correct ourselves.

11. Release it.

Let it go. There is no need to drag this issue like a bag of rocks. Every time we hold onto the guilt or shame, it's like adding a rock to a bag we have to carry. After a while, that bag gets incredibly heavy.

Let it go. You may be the only one aware of this anyway, so leave it behind. Unpack it from your bag, and leave it here. Learn the lessons, and release the guilt and shame. It's no longer yours to carry. You carried it until you could learn the lesson, and now you have. It's done.

So let it be written, so let it be done.

Shifting Gears

I carried a lot of junk, much that wasn't mine even though I thought it was. I needed a little help to let it go. My colleague helped me identify what I'd done or been that was suspect. By getting all my pieces out on the table, I could look them over. My guilt and shame felt like a huge bag of rocks, but the pieces lying on the table weren't so big or scary. Bits that looked so significant when I was three or 23 seemed different now. Perhaps it was the vantage point of age or seeing the whole picture rather than only my limited perspective. Was I wrong in some incidents? Absolutely. I made mistakes, some age appropriate, some learning-in-progress, some from giving in to my lesser nature. Was I falsely blamed at times? Absolutely.

Recognizing the multifaceted elements of my guilt and shame was the start. From there I could choose what to do with the bits that no longer fit (chuck them out). I could see what I needed to change or repair or where I otherwise needed to take action. Some became the normal scars and bruises of living.

And I could see where I needed to change my thinking, to stop filling my mind with negative chatter about these experiences. If I stopped digging up the old stuff, it could stay buried and return to the usefulness of compost. If I watered that with more positive thoughts and experiences, the space would produce good fruit. Focusing on the good reinforces it and leaves no room for the guilt and shame that no longer belongs to us.

And I grew to feel more positive, happier even, and that meant I didn't need to comfort myself so much, which saved a bunch of unplanned calories. Bonus!

For Your Consideration

Did you do the exercise? If so, how free do you feel right now? Amazing, isn't it?

If you didn't do the exercise, consider how that is working for or against you. How could you facilitate this exercise for yourself? Would it help to have a friend or counselor present with you?

What would help you work through it?

How will you make peace with yourself and others?

How will you release your guilt or shame?

*The emotional satisfaction of navigating a food fest well
is more gratifying than the momentary food or drink.*

CHAPTER EIGHT

Holy Days and Holidays

Quick Start Guide: Things That Work

Find as many quotes, statements, and pictures as you can fit on a page or two that encourage and affirm you and feed your heart. Find quotes in pictures on social media or do a search on the web. Make a collage, leave it as a list, place individual quotes where you can see them, and do what makes it work for you.

Then read them daily. Put them where you can see them and allow them to feed your soul. Inspiration will feed your intention, and the magic bullet for change—weight or otherwise—is the power of your intention. Believe in yourself. You may not yet see the physical evidence of your ultimate goal, and getting to that goal is a process. A huge chunk of the process is staying motivated, being inspired to keep at it. If you can't quite believe it about yourself at the moment, believe it of your best potential self. Find quotes that work for you. Or pen your own.

Here's a starter from Henry James: "Nothing of the senses will ever satisfy the soul."

Holidays hijack our best laid nutrition and exercise plans. They just do. There should be extra credit for maintaining during holidays, and it is possible with a good plan even if you indulge in a few holiday favorites.

It's okay. It's a day, and it's a day of celebration. In many cultures, celebration means feasting. So feast. Enjoy every bite, chewing thoroughly, squeezing the flavor from every morsel. When you stop enjoying it, or when you feel satisfied, stop eating.

You did catch the point of it being *a day*, didn't you? Does that sound like I'm being a killjoy? In the States, we have the five-week food orgy we call The Holidays. Thanksgiving to New Year's day is often a season of indulgence encompassing several national and religious holidays. It gets special attention and intention toward a Super Bowl of our favorite foods. National and religious holidays always include seasonal themed foods, and weeks of planning and cooking go into the calendar from November to January.

My mother and I spent at least two weekends creating all kinds of special confections that said, "Christmas" to us. Most were really sweet and rich, and few were designated as dessert for the actual holiday. No, these were stored in tins on the sideboard and used as snacks, too-oft-sought-out-snacks as evidenced by my waistline. I could easily gain seven to 10 pounds every December. Bonbons of various sorts, candies that resembled fruits but were just sweet concoctions in the shape of said fruit, pecan pralines, peanut patties, butterscotch haystacks, fudge, divinity, various layered bars, and cakes (which incidentally made terrific breakfast alternatives, but I digress). A few salty things like homemade savory cereal, pretzel, and nut mix; chocolate-coated cracker sandwiches with a layer of peanut butter; and nuts were always available. We indulged with gusto.

In my growing up years, my family of origin and I were always eating beyond the point of satisfaction on holidays, well beyond. That overstuffed feeling seemed to be half the point. If we weren't miserable, we didn't feel we had truly enjoyed the holiday. We couldn't waste the leftovers, of course! Although we seemed oblivious to how we "waisted" the food as we kept right on eating until they were gone, hopefully by New Year's day. We laughed at ourselves, and remorse came quickly. After stringing together several days of excess, that remorse came in truckloads. What were we thinking?

We weren't, and that was the problem. We were feeding our needs and cherishing memories and trying to either fill or re-create them with Hello Dolly cake, my nan's turkey and dressing, or fudge— which, I have to admit, I don't really even like as it was so sweet and rich that it made my teeth hurt. Still, it was part of the holiday, and I ate it anyway. Oy vey, goodness me!

The foods changed around the calendar, but we saw holidays as three-day food orgies: The Eve, The Day, The Leftovers. It was ridiculously silly, and breaking out of that pattern helped me. With a bounty of rich foods that we make especially for the holidays, I often gain a pound or two over the days of celebration, but it's no longer the seven to ten pounds that took weeks to offload.

Enjoy the feast, and stop when you are satisfied. Then return to the plan the next morning—or at least nearer to your plan if it's the long holiday season. One or two days won't tank your efforts, but a week and a half will. The only remedy is to get back on that horse and ride. If you've gained a pound or two, do what you know to do and make it work.

One of the pitfalls is thinking of The Holidays as a season of overeating rather than as specific holiday feast DAYS. Rather than throwing out our nutrition guidelines for the month, we can enjoy each day or eve, and make a plan for the other days in between when every work and play place is having a party or holiday "goodies." If we focus on enjoying the feast of the eve and day and practice a little restraint in between, there will be less to sort out afterward, and we'll still enjoy the celebration and skip the recurring guilt of overindulgence.

Holidays are filled with memories and nostalgia, photos and films, traditions, and families. Except when they aren't—or aren't any more. This kicks up all kinds of emotional "stuff." Whether it's a memory of the way the holiday always *was* or the expectation of how we want it to *be*, that's plenty to drive emotional eating. If it didn't turn out as we hoped, we may turn to foods that taste like the holiday always did. We'll take a taste if we can't get the reality.

One year, my husband and I set out around nine in the morning, heading west to his family's home for the holiday. We packed the car with gifts and with the foods we wanted to contribute to the celebration. Just over halfway there, we were caught in an uncharacteristically sudden and intense ice storm with a little bit of snow but not enough to provide traction. Texas doesn't normally do a white Christmas, and the roads were absolutely clear until the moment we crossed the line where they weren't, and all traffic in front of us came to an absolute stop an hour and a half into our journey.

We crept along for over an hour covering fewer than 10 miles and decided to abandon our hopes of getting to my in-law's as the storm intensified to the west. Many in front of us were stuck for the night on a major interstate highway. On Christmas Eve. With almost every business closing by two in the afternoon.

We managed to turn around, and by then, the weather was moving east faster than we were. So we crept home at 20 miles per hour. It was tedious, and we were disappointed to miss the family gathering, and as the hours wore on, we were HUNGRY. Nothing was open, and we feared that if we left the interstate, we wouldn't be able to get back on.

"I have Chex Mix!" I shouted to the dear one. We had all the snacks we had made for the festivities—candies, Chex Mix, some fudge. We even had a couple of sodas and water. Definitely not healthy, but by three o'clock, breakfast had long since digested. It would tide us over.

I shifted into "wife" mode as we crept along, thinking about the holiday dinner and what we might have at home. Ah, I had all the

WHAT'S REALLY EATING YOU? · 105

ingredients for the dressing with me. We had some turkey in the freezer, likely some green beans, too. Then it dawned. "Michael, dear, we have the cheesecake."

While we were still exhausted after a drive that should have taken an hour and a half that took over five, I was comforted having what I considered the essential ingredients for a Christmas dinner. Our memories have deep roots in our senses of taste and scent.

And we had a white Christmas, which is so rare in Texas that it has its own brand of magic.

A Practical Holiday Plan

1. **For those memories that make the holidays sweeter or harder, as they do both, identify them.**

   Find that feeling, the joy of the perfect holiday, the haunting memory, or loss that drives your eating, and face it. It's like removing a splinter rather than leaving it to get infected. Take it out, look at it, and choose how you want to deal with it. Perhaps how you've always done it isn't working for you anymore, so find a way that works in your favor. We'll shift lanes in traffic to move forward even just a car length, but sometimes we stick behind a grumpy memory like we're trapped. Why do we do that to ourselves?

   If the joy is in the festive consumption, then make good choices about the foods you take. Do you like it? Or is it just what you've always eaten, and therefore it's part of the holiday? When you do like it, take it slowly. If you say you enjoy it, then enjoy it. No regrets, no guilt, no swallowing whole. Take time to enjoy it.

   Perhaps you need a little more or a little less time on your own. You may need time to reflect, and some time alone will do you good. Or perhaps you get too much of that and need to get out and interact more.

Perhaps you need to shift your focus from what you've lost to what you can now give to others. Many charities have added opportunities to participate, and what people often find is that when they give to others, they get so much more back from the experience. Or maybe you need to talk this out with a counselor, mentor, or friend.

None of the sugary, salty, or otherwise rich "goodies" will fill that space. They just won't. Nor will those indulgences make the holiday any sweeter. It's not the food; it's the association with the memory that holds your heart. Separate the memory and savor that.

2. **The season is merry and full of good things, so have some of it—I'm not a fan of deprivation.**

However, consider cutting your portion size to maybe 75% of what you might normally take. Enjoy every bite of it, luxuriate in the flavor and texture. If you love it, honor it by putting it on a plate and paying attention as you eat it. Don't eat standing in the pantry or in front of the refrigerator, swallowing it so quickly that you don't even taste it. Take the time to enjoy it. Then see if you still want that last 25%. If you do, follow the same protocol and enjoy it.

3. **Balance your calorie intake.**

If you overindulge at one meal, choose something lighter for the next meal. Gauge your actual hunger, not your want. We may equate holidays with permission to indulge our gluttony, but do you really want to choose that for yourself? Will that work toward your goal? Check your compass and adjust your path accordingly.

4. **Add a little exercise; a walk is enough, even a brief 10-minute walk is useful.**

    I lost 25 pounds doing no more exercise than walking my dog. You get a stress relief bonus with a short walk outside—even if it's only from the parking lot into the mall for your Christmas shopping. Take six to eight deep, connected breaths, and you'll be less harried as well. Deep breathing is a stress buster, and you can do that anywhere.

5. **Be sensible.**

    You don't have to "DIET" during the holidays, but sensible choices most of the season will help launch you into the New Year without extra to lose. Choose the things you most enjoy rather than anything and everything. If it's not your favorite, leave it. Is something you only marginally care for worth the extra attention you will have to invest in the new year? Are you willing to sacrifice one of your allowed indulgences later to make up for this food that you don't really care for but is available?

    I don't get the whole gummy snack thing. Nor licorice whips. Only some versions of caramel. If it isn't chocolate, nut-based, coconut, truffle/nougat, or creamy, it's not really worth the calories for me. Find your favorites and what you're willing to choose. Alter your thinking, and the displays will not be so tempting.

6. **Focus on enjoying the people you love and the joy their presence brings you.**

    Holidays are occasions for gathering with people we love and care for. Most of the time. Hopefully. Be present along with bringing presents. Watch how quickly focusing on enjoying the company of those you love can fill your heart and distract you from over-filling your plate.

I used to say I could never be distracted from eating. Then I got really engaged in a conversation with someone, and time evaporated along with my appetite. Perhaps it's an activity for you. Plan opportunities for whatever truly distracts you so that time gets away from you. Even if it's over a meal, you may find yourself so filled by the experience that food is a less important component.

Most of all, enjoy the holidays. Temptations will lie on every desk and table almost willing you to partake—and you should in moderation. Depriving ourselves of holiday party foods is a recipe for a food binge, and if we plan for them, we can maintain our moderate approach. The key is wanting to reach that goal enough to make choices consistent with your time line. If wanting the food now is more important, recognize that it's okay. It's a choice you can make, so own it. You'll have a bit more work to do in the new year if that's still important to you, or you won't and your body will reflect that. Either is fine. It's still your choice.

Shifting Gears

My no-sweat holiday exercise:

Imagine your perfect holiday: who would be there, what you would be doing, how the hours would go, what you would eat and when, where you would be. Get creative and imagine the season in all its joyful glory... and realism. You can't control others, but you can control how you respond to them—so imagine yourself responding in the best possible way for who you want to be. What would be the perfect response to the person tempting you with more than you want? What would be the perfect way to end that holiday party or Christmas dinner? In your best self, how would you walk through this season? Imagine it in full sensory and emotional detail.

Now imagine what you normally do—in full sensory and emotional detail.

What are the differences? Which parts do you want to keep and which do you want to do differently?

Athletes visualize themselves going through every step and motion of their sport. It helps them accomplish each step of the process—they see themselves making a shot or move perfectly. Part of that is learning to recognize how each moment feels, which muscles are involved, timing, and so forth. They are more likely to know what to do in a pressure situation if they've visualized their best response and action.

Visualization helps me with holidays and year-round weight management. It triggers something in our brains, releasing "feel good" chemicals rather than the stress response, and that's a win any day of the year. If I know a challenge is approaching, I visualize my best response. The emotional satisfaction of navigating a food fest well is so much more gratifying than the momentary flavor and sensation of that food or drink. It doesn't always work out exactly as I hoped and, yet, more often than not, I do better than I have in previous situations. Life is practice.

For Your Consideration

What quotes, statements, pictures, etc. encourage and affirm your heart? How did placing them where you would see them affect your days?

Consider the next holiday on the calendar. How have you walked through them before, and how will you do this year differently?

What memories make the holiday for you?

What foods do you traditionally consume? Do you still like them or simply consume them because you always have?

How will choosing to do things differently help, hurt, challenge, or encourage you and those around you?

New Year, New You is fine, but I like New Year, True Me.

CHAPTER NINE

Resolutions and Resolving Issues

Quick Start Guide: Things That Work

So that food we can't say no to? Enjoy every bite of it, relish the flavor and texture when you choose to have it. Rather than fighting it, plan a time to enjoy it. Prohibiting yourself from having it at all creates or exacerbates that "gotta have it" craving. Or perhaps I'm the only one who responds to prohibition with a redheaded, "Just stand back and watch me." Frail creature of dust, I am.

Finding a way to make it fit into your plan now and again relieves that pressure and almost makes it respectable with an air of responsibility. There are no foods we love that we must give up forever. None. Not a one. Abstaining forever, unless your health demands it, is not practical, and I know I wouldn't stick to it. One of the joys of life is enjoying food treats now and, again, particularly those that have a memory attached. It's okay now and again. Planning for its inclusion manages the craving as well as our preferences.

However, if it pops up one day off your plan and you just can't leave it alone for whatever reason, make it count. Honor it.

Take the time to enjoy it. Give yourself permission. Set the table, and use a plate.

Once you come back to yourself, make a few notes about what was going on. What prompted this undeniable need? Be as specific as possible. Once we know what creates an issue for us, we can plan a better strategy for meeting our needs in a different way. If we meet the needs of our hearts and bodies, cravings and compulsions are less likely to jump up and bite us.

Every new year brings opportunities, whether it's January, your birthday, or any other version of a new calendar year. In January, the world is aware of making resolutions, and whether or not we make them says a lot about our state of mind.

Have we grown cynical, believing we can't really change, and therefore just don't think about resolutions?

Are we full of belief and make them every year, and do pretty well at keeping them?

Are we full of belief but short on conviction about our abilities to keep them?

Do we make the same resolutions every year as a kind of running joke?

At the first staff meeting of January early in my career in a helping profession, I was rather shocked by the response of my coworkers when I asked about resolutions and made the mistake of saying so. They laughed. Naïve I was, they said. Lofty-minded. Romantic idealism coupled with immaturity. Snort. A good dose of life will cure that, they said.

I was aghast. I thought our purpose was in helping others grow personally and spiritually, and this group of people I was supposed to learn from and emulate saw this cultural "fresh start" as a silly, romantic notion. Obviously, it still has an impact. Note to self.

It took me a long time to return to the idea and several others I'd jettisoned at their behest—more than a year after being away from that group, but when my habit for resolutions returned, it had morphed into more of a goal setting practice. That works for me. It may not work for everyone, or it might if given the smallest wisp of a chance. You get to decide that for yourself.

Reaching goals is also about mindset. Do we believe we can reach goals and maintain them? We yo-yo for a lot of years, and it begins to seem like the natural order of things. It's not. Yet do we believe that? The experiences of many around us indicate getting to our goal weight is a short-lived goal. Get there, gain back a couple, do well for a period of time until we get off the plan again, indulge one too many times, and then we're out of the mindset and our weight rises. Again. Who knows how long it will take me to get back in the right frame of mind to tackle the issue again!

What do you believe about your ability to maintain a goal weight?

Sometimes the long-standing issues like weight management are most challenging, and yet they are also the most rewarding when we do conquer them. How would it be if we chose to believe rather than beginning the journey doubting? Just because that's what's happened before doesn't mean it will happen this time—it comes back to your intention. Do you intend to reach your goal? Genuinely now. Do you intend to reach it? Seriously? Do you intend to stay there? Or is this simply a plastic bandage to help you feel better for a couple of weeks before you sink back into indulging your cravings?

If you begin with such doubt about your ability to reach a goal, maybe the goal or your intention need some adjustment to avoid the doubt that becomes a self-fulfilling prophecy.

If you believe you can't reach your goal, what's behind that? Is it experience? After so many years of setting myself a weight loss goal, I know the paradox of hope and failure *again*. Yet there were other goals that I set and achieved, so what was up with the weight? The clincher or glitch is different for everyone. Sometimes it's an issue of focus, which we do get to choose, and that focus carries us to the outcome. Sometimes it's an issue of circumstances or priorities, and again, we may have more control over that than we will admit to ourselves.

That sounds a bit harsh, and yet it's a conundrum I know and loathe in myself. I can do it, and I will do it when I'm in that mindset. The question comes in how to manufacture that mindset on demand rather than awaiting the mood to strike us. We do it for other goals or tasks, don't we?

We completed projects and exams for education. We complete tasks set by our careers. We do our taxes every year—and who in their right mind wants to do that? We clean house or mow our lawns, give the dog a bath, take our cars in for oil and repair, find ways to manage encounters with our crazy, doddering aunties at family gatherings, and we complete hosts of other activities and commitments we don't really want to do but manage to motivate ourselves to complete.

We manufacture a mindset to fulfill what we see as responsibilities in many other arenas. What's up with the weight thing? Or any other goal we find difficult?

At the beginning of my journey, I finished the five-week food orgy at least seven pounds heavier than I was in November. Okay, 10, which happened to be five pounds heavier than I had been in September. Having cake for breakfast will do that. I didn't really believe I could lose more than five or six pounds, and from experience, I believed I would gain and lose those same five or six pounds many times throughout the year. I'd done that a lot over the years. Why would this year truly be any different? When I popped back up to my all-time high at various times over the years, I'd get motivated and work really hard to reduce my weight 15 to 20 pounds, and then I'd get stuck and never lose the rest or even begin to approach my ultimate goal. Then I'd do the five up, five down tango for a while. I felt chained to that weight. Getting under that threshold was hard work, and it never lasted for me. It was almost like a ricochet, and if I actually told someone I'd reached a certain marker, I'd rocket up again.

Shifting that one belief that "I'd fail yet again" helped. Why would I fail again? It wasn't like I hadn't succeeded in actually losing the weight. I knew how to do that. What could I do to help myself succeed for the long-term and actually get to my ultimate goal weight and stay there? I could see potential for real change even if I hadn't experienced it yet. Then I learned the skills and dealt with my emotional stuff, and both made a difference and continue to make a difference.

Those emotional calories are dense and clingy. They are the hardest to lose, and they pop up no matter what the stressor. When I disarmed the triggers that set off my emotional eating, I didn't need to eat to soothe and comfort myself anymore. Untangling that component helped me reduce more pounds that have stayed off my body, and a few more have melted away since then without starving, without deprivation, and without crazy hard exercise. When we don't have to counter the excess calories from emotional eating, we have fewer calories to burn that makes our efforts more effective. Normal fluctuations from week to week are just that: fluctuations. Those pounds don't take up permanent residence.

Goal Setting for Real Change

A goal for real change is not an endpoint. We think of goals as finish lines, and that often fuels our yo-yo weight. We get to the goal and think, "YEA! We can have whatever food we've been missing all this time!" Rather than choosing appropriate portions, we go crazy, and boom! Our weight jumps up yet again.

It helped me to think of my weight goal as a new position. When we have a goal for our career, we often shift companies or responsibilities, or maybe we get a promotion. If we kept going back to our old job/desk/tasks/routine, we wouldn't keep the new one long.

We set a goal, we achieved it, and now we act or work in light of that new achievement. The old job is no longer ours nor do we want it. The new weight is ours to keep, and we have to make choices based on maintaining that weight.

At five feet three inches, I could eat a certain number of calories to maintain 150, 180, or 200 pounds. To hold at 130 or 120, the numbers changed, and to stay around 115, it requires fewer calories to keep my body humming. The engine is more efficient because I'm not dragging around an extra 10, 20, or 50 pounds of fat. Logically it makes sense, but synchronizing the logic and emotion took some time. My "wanter" can be greedy, and I have to manage that. Still, my body is fine, but it's that funky belief that we're being deprived that complicates the issue. It's not deprivation to only take what we need. Somehow with food, we seem to be greedy when we'd condemn that from others and in other situations.

We have to go back to the logical equation. Look at the number of calories you can eat and maintain the weight you desire. Write it down so you can look at it in black and white. We've done enough dieting to know our basic range of calories, don't we? To lose, we had to reduce that number, so to maintain that weight we get a few calories back in our menu. By "a few," I don't mean a thousand extra calories a day. "A few" as in adding 250 to 500 per day if that's what works for you. We also have an idea of what our upper limit number is. Find the number and macronutrients that create your best fuel mix. Nutritional science is incredibly complex and individual, so what works for you WORKS FOR YOU. Find your numbers and stick near them.

Once at our goal, the old weight and size is no longer an option. I'm at my best size, at the best weight for me. How does someone at this weight and size now act? What choices would she make? Write it down if it helps you.

It was easy when I thought of the new clothing size. I had more than one size in my closet, so I separated them even though some of them were pieces I hadn't been able to wear as much as my frugal mind wanted in order to justify their original purchase. I had to be strong and put them in a bag to either go out or for donation. No more three or four sizes where I could see them. One size. One size only. These were my clothes now. There were no other options. If they got a little snug, that was a signal to pay attention for a couple of days to return to my position.

This is what people with a consistent weight do. If they splurge (a word of censure in itself), they balance out either before in anticipation of the splurge or afterward. In her book, French Women Don't Get Fat, Mireille Guiliano said the American association of eating with sin or guilt is quite foreign to her culture. French women do not deny themselves a pleasure to teach their greedy selves a lesson. "The only purpose of withholding some pleasure is so we can more fully enjoy everything else for having it in proper balance."

Fascinating concept: Withhold a pleasure now so I can fully enjoy something else later. Not punish myself before or after. Not deprive myself. I've said it many times: I'm saving my appetite for _____. I know it's not really wise to skip breakfast completely as it often sets off binge behavior later, but my grandmother's rolls and pies were really, really worth the effort of eating lightly so I could truly enjoy every bite at lunchtime. Planning our day and monitoring our intake is not punishment. It's being responsible.

We make responsible choices with work, we do it with our budgets (mostly), and we do it with hygiene and for caring for others. The consequences are different. Aren't they? Often the consequences become the greatest motivator.

The consequences of our diets are different in that the consequences can be delayed. Perhaps we won't fit into that dress for that special event, and catty comments may sting, but a few days later, we're back in our sweatpants feeling cozy again. Our health is greatly affected by our weight and nutritional balance, and yet the effects of that may not show up for years, and maybe we will be in that small group that isn't affected at all. Uh huh.

When we're trying to retrain our habits during the whirlwind of a party, the holidays, or an emotional upheaval, it is hard. It is. And yet it is more than possible if we choose to stay focused on what we are getting from the efforts. The rewards do multiply. The magic bullet is still the power of our intentions.

Method

Choose a goal. Seems obvious, but the obvious is still a first step. Is it a weight or size or exercise goal? Or maybe it's a habit to form or extract, a learning goal, or an activity goal. Whatever your goal is, this method will provide some structure to support it.

Choose a date for accomplishment. My resolution had always been to lose 10 to 20 pounds sometime in the year, but I had no fixed date. Always needed to lose more, but I thought 10 or 20 was a good place to start. Once I set a target date, I made progress. Fix a date. Make it real.

Make it specific. Choose an app to help you keep track or write down your goal. My goal was based on a weight I thought I could have a fair shot of achieving, and then I had a secondary number that would be my bonus goal. It helped to think of the first number as an incremental goal rather than as a sort of range that would be fine with me. When there is no specific goal, it's harder to measure progress. We're just sort of spinning on the string and maybe losing the thread.

Create some form of accountability. Everyone responds differently to accountability, so find the brand that works for you. Gretchen Rubin's book, *Better Than Before*, categorizes people into one of four categories in response to expectations and accountability. My type finds it very easy to help others with their goals, and yet I can't do that for myself. I flake out on my own, and I need someone to hold me accountable in some way. I need someone who expects me to be at the gym or to do a workout or follow a good food plan. When I work with clients on their weight management, I'm much more aware of my nutrition plan, size, weight, and exercise. When I'm on a deadline, I'll likely complete my task ahead of time. When someone is expecting me to be somewhere, I will be there even if I don't want to attend. Exterior accountability works for me. When I was losing my weight, I had a friend who checked up on my progress, and knowing she would ask kept me motivated when my own intention flagged.

Make it manageable. Choosing an unrealistic goal is being mean to yourself, so be kind. What is realistic for the time period you've set? Apps will give you feedback on your goal. Choose intermediate goals, and make them manageable. One client said, "But I have sooooooo much to lose. It will take a year!" Perhaps so, but you'll be a year further along anyway. Do you want to still be where you are in a year? Or do you want to be nearer to your goal?

Create rewards for intermediate goals. Everyone has thresholds of significance. Any time I crossed over to a number ending in two or seven, I felt the difference. I felt leaner, even when I was only beginning. It was a great feeling that was a reward in itself, but I had a system of rewards as I reached an accomplishment. It's often best to make it a non-food reward, and if the reward helps you move even further toward your goal, all the better. Make it motivating, make it personal, and make it possible within your lifestyle and budget. What motivates you? Even if it's something you might do anyway under particular circumstances, tie it to your goal and follow through. How often do we blow off something that will encourage us with thoughts of it being unnecessary? We'd be all over encouraging someone else in the same situation, wouldn't we? So be kind enough to yourself to follow through on your intermediate rewards. Keep that ultimate goal reward in sight, but small and incremental rewards are encouraging.

Get a vision. Find a picture of yourself at that goal weight or size. If you've never been at that size long enough to take a picture, choose a photo of someone else and attach a photo of your face to it. Or put some of your skinny clothes or a goal outfit where you can see it. I had this one pair of jeans from the one time in my life when I was near my goal weight that I hadn't worn in 17 years, but I couldn't let go of them. I left them hanging very visibly in the closet, and each morning they motivated me to pay attention to my behavior and choices.

Can you see yourself there? I had a hard time envisioning it as I had so many more mental images as well as photos of myself at a heavier weight. I had spent a lot more time there, and we are very good at imagining all the worst possible scenarios. When you are in your most positive frame of mind, turn that around to the best possible scenario. What will it look like when you are where you want to be? What will it sound like, feel like? See yourself in *that* dress or bikini or *those* jeans and imagine how that will feel. When you are tempted by something that isn't on your plan—whether that's skipping too many workouts or ingesting something that will tank your nutrition—remember what you will look like when you reach your goal. In your best moment, would you still want it? Feel it emotionally, but also touch it, hear it, see it, taste it, breathe it in. Focusing on the outcomes in our senses can straighten our path.

Believe you can accomplish the goal, and if you don't already believe it, enlist someone who believes in you enough to support you until you do. If you don't believe it's possible, well, Henry Ford said, "If you think you can do a thing or you think you can't do a thing, you're right." You're intelligent, competent, talented, interesting, and capable. What have you ever *wanted* to do that you haven't accomplished?

Want it, and affirm that you want it. If you don't want it, no encouragement will help you. Resolutions and goals fail because we don't want it more than we want that piece of cheesecake /macchiato/ sugar or starch package of whatever sort that tempts you/overindulgence in the moment of temptation. In the cold light of day, what do you truly want most? Will that Twinkie get you there?

Get congruent with your goal. When you want the Twinkie more than your goal, then you're not quite settled on that goal. When you truly want your goal more, you will get there. Think about what will happen when you get to that goal. How will you feel? What can you do? What could you wear that you can't wear now? Find the element that motivates you. That propels you toward your goal.

What do you actually see now? I had a hard time with this. I'd been fat for over 40 years, so I didn't really remember myself as thin, and I couldn't see much progress toward the goal. I might have been close for about five minutes as I lost weight for my wedding day, but that didn't last long as the uptrend of the yo-yo took hold. I could still see the fat around my belly, and albeit a smaller amount, it was still a little pooch. That's how I saw myself, and I focused on the protrusion. It was almost as if I couldn't see myself as anything other than as a chunk. I referred to my legs as fence posts. Anytime I approached the vicinity of my goal, I still saw myself as hefty because I was only looking for the negative rather than looking for what had improved. I didn't see the slenderer waist; I saw that I wasn't yet down to the size I wanted. I was focused on what wasn't yet right rather than looking for improvement. That didn't help me.

What do we say to ourselves? When we've overindulged, do we accuse and shame ourselves for our size? When we're irritated or angry, do we call ourselves names? "You fat tub of lard!" Or do we question our intelligence because we're struggling? "Stupid, stupid, stupid" ever come up in your mind after a derailment of intentions? Our words affect how we feel, and if we need soothing, we return to what has traditionally worked for us. Maybe it's partly because we can't really trust ourselves. I wouldn't treat a friend as poorly as I treat myself. If I had a friend who spoke to me as harshly as I speak to myself, I wouldn't trust them, so why would I trust myself?

Be kind. Treat yourself like you would treat your best friend. Be gracious and compassionate. We're doing the best we can in the circumstances with the tools we've learned, and we're now learning new ones—and we're not proficient yet, so we must give ourselves some grace. It's a process.

In the meantime, add in some affirmative words. I'm thin. I'm shapely. I'm trim. I'm skinny in all the right ways. I'm learning and growing while my body is shrinking.

Find the words that work for you, but make them kind and affirming. Your heart will notice, and your body will respond.

Resolving the Issue

What if we just addressed the issues that plague us? We tend to manage issues or create alibis for our weaknesses, but what if we resolved them or strengthened ourselves?

You can do that?

Isn't it fascinating that we should wonder?

At risk of being branded as too lofty minded again, more issues than we care to admit can be resolved when we take time to address them and make the necessary changes. We do it for other issues. We problem solve for work, to create time for vacations, for our families, even more making household schedules work. Yet when we speak of doing something like jettisoning excess weight, we say, "Yes, but how do you do that with a family and a job and responsibilities and, and, and ..."

Sometimes, you just do. Check in with your accountability style and build a solution. I was texting back and forth with a colleague when I realized I made a lot of excuses for why I wasn't doing the things I felt were important. I was in the midst of one of those tasks, realizing it was taking longer than it should, likely due to stopping every couple of minutes to thumb type a new text. Yet I didn't want to stop texting my friend. You know what it's like—some friends think in ways you don't, so they are that much more intriguing and they set off unfamiliar thought patterns that take us places we'd never get on our own. Fantastic conversations even by text. Yet the task at hand was supposed to be more important.

We shared a sense of getting caught up in trying to meet expectations, prioritize tasks, fulfilling duty. Prioritizing is hard, until it isn't.

It's amazing that when I have a hard deadline, and I'm trying to fit in a certain number of tasks before that deadline, the priority of each gets very clear. That can wait, that was a "wish I could," that's just never going to happen, and that must be done completely in the next XX minutes, and we don't feel guilty for shirking a detail. The deadline-wielding task or event is the priority, and the extra tasks fall away.

Resolving an issue can be prioritized just as clearly. When we get tired enough of feeling a certain way, we tend to do whatever it takes to no longer feel that way. Up to now, we had no problem choosing the chocolate, the cake, the glass of wine to dull the feeling, to soothe over that hurt. We do it naturally already, although we need to find a different soother. What are other options that will soothe?

There are demands on you. There are lists of things to do longer than any human being can accomplish. You do what looks good for those around you, what feels important, what is necessary, what will help you with x, y, z, and if you don't do it, you'll feel guilty for letting someone down. The "all or nothing" thinking is engaged, and then you're so tired that you feel you're the only one missing out. A cupcake will help! Until it doesn't. And it doesn't resolve the issues; it only acts as a bandage for the moment.

We can use the principle for our benefit. We already recognize single-minded focus. What would it take to get you where you want to go or to how you want to feel? Seriously.

Identify an issue you want to tackle. One. We can't attack all of our issues at once. Be kind to yourself and choose one.

What is the smallest measure of a task you could accomplish right now or today to make some effort toward resolving the issue? Don't get caught up in how big this issue is for you—that's your comfort zone guarding its territory. Focus on one step toward it. Focus on one pound not 50, focus on choosing a more positive outlook in this moment not winning the "Happy Soul of the Year" award, focus on unpacking one piece of frustration from your baggage not forgiving the person who crushed you, focus on keeping one drawer uncluttered today rather than the whole house. Focus on one piece of the battleground, not the war. One effort toward your goal is enough for this moment. Then try another one. String together several over time, and you can see your progress.

Do you need help? Sometimes we've been battling an issue for so long, we can't see how it has permeated our lives. An objective person can help see the tendrils and help us untangle them. A friend can reframe our points of view and gives us another perspective on the situation. An encouraging word can help us see where we're making progress, and a framework for accountability can help us stay on course.

One step at a time, one issue at a time. Focus on the next step, and glance up once in a while to check your progress toward the ultimate goal.

And be kind to yourself. You've probably beaten yourself up long enough over this issue. Has beating yourself helped yet? Ever? Ready to try something different? Something affirming? Be kind.

Shifting Gears

All the marketing for the New Year tends to be along the lines of being a new you, and I bought into that year after year. Yet, what was so wrong with the me that was here already? Maybe not all the protective masks and coping mechanisms and contortions I'd created of myself, but the authentic me, the true me. I could dust off all the masks and polish myself up a bit. Or I could drop the masks, address the issues I was avoiding with coping mechanisms, and straighten out the contortions by just being myself. New Year, New You is fine, but

I like the "New Year, True You." Being who we are is so much easier in the end, and it's easy because it's true.

Finding what was true for me and valuing that was a significant discovery for my progress. Life pummels us a bit, and we do begin to think we are the problem. Maybe instead, in our true form we are the answer. It takes much less effort, and the results tend to be more effective when we're simply content with who we are, our choices, our skills and talents, our personalities. It requires less compensation and brings more fulfillment, which for me meant less comfort eating. Those comfort calories are dense, and if I worked at being at peace with myself, I didn't need the soothing. Identifying the True Me and what she needs saved a lot calories and effort. She doesn't need soothing because she's happy just being herself. What a concept!

For Your Consideration

What's the food you need to give yourself permission to include in your long-term plan? When you have it, how will you honor it? What plate or dish will you use? Will you use a paper or a cloth napkin? What will your time of honoring and enjoying that food look like? Feel like?

Can you believe you will make changes to help you reach your goal? If you doubt it, what's behind that?

How will you look, feel, behave, interact when you reach your goal?

Set a goal. Be specific. Make it manageable.

How do you respond to accountability? What will help you reach your goal?

What are your intermediate goals and rewards? List them. Both parts: goals *and* rewards.

What's your vision of yourself at that goal?

Are you congruent with that goal? If not, what do you need to allow yourself to be congruent?

How can you resolve your issues rather than create more alibis?

"No quick joke or explosion can replace a single human emotion."
Jack Klugman

Or in the realm of weight management . . .

*No crash diet or hot trend can replace
consistently making good choices.*

CHAPTER TEN

Diet—Ugh!

Quick Start Guide: Things That Work

What do you need?

Really?

Ask yourself often, and the more you ask, the more you will learn what drives your needs for food and indulgence.

When you're hitting your door, and you feel like you're emotionally starving even if you've had a meal, what is it you're starving for? Is food an anesthetic? Is it an indulgence? Or are you looking for a transcendent moment in an ordinary day?

Are you seeking something salty to enhance a bland experience? Something sweet to help an experience go down more easily? Something vinegary or tart to match an ill temper or cope with an ill-tempered encounter?

What is the origin of this need? Find that, find another way to meet that need, and you will both get your need met in an efficient and resoundingly effective way, and the food will not be necessary. Saves a bunch of calories, and it has no negative effect on your insulin or other body processes.

Often we need help to delve this deeply into our stuff. A counselor, coach, or trusted friend could be invaluable to facing your stuff so you can skip stuffing your face.

It's been done to death. This diet and that, this cleanse, that dietary supplement. For best results: Pick one and stick to it. They will all work for someone, maybe everyone if we're faithful and can follow it without getting too grumpy or feeling starved. Follow the directions and guidelines for a designated length of time and see how it works for you. If this one doesn't work, try another until you find the one that leaves you feeling satisfied as well as allows you to manage your weight. This is training in the end, and we cobble together foods, recipes, habits, and choices that work for us long term.

When I try a new recipe, I always stick to the measurements, ingredients, and methods the first time I make it. After that, I can tinker with it, and the results were often better than the original recipe. When trying a new diet, however, although I'd follow it faithfully for a time and get good results from the scale, my hunger or energy levels led to tinkering which usually led to weight gain for me. That tinkering more often involved a kind of designated cheating, which meant I wasn't following the guidelines closely enough. Hello, Self-Sabotage.

Even in tinkering, we still have to follow the guidelines to get the result because our bodies are complex. Once you get the hang of a particular plan, search for variety in recipes that fit the plan. After a couple of weeks, you'll either see the results or won't, and if it isn't working for you, try another one and follow those guidelines. Most plans do work while we follow them whether we find it easy or hard, constrictive or wonderful, satisfying or leaving us starved. As often repeated, all diets work, but not all diets work for everyone. Variations in metabolism, activity, preferences, consumption, and so on and so on ad nauseam are individual, so find the one that keeps you satisfied and fits your lifestyle and preferences and leaves you feeling good, energetic, and happy.

Plan to Succeed

Wake up, now. Are you with me? We can do this. If we can reclaim hope and find belief in ourselves, if we can harness our intention to make "good for me" choices, we succeed. I know. Forty years of efforts (insert your long-haul effort number here) and losing a thousand pounds—and regaining it—makes it hard to believe. However, as we make structural emotional changes, fueled by confidence in the potential of our best selves, we can succeed—and stay there. After those 40 years, I'm 4 years and counting at my goal weight because of those structural changes—they helped me stick to my plan.

With any diet or change in plan, we start out well. We're motivated. We may even get up early to pack our lunch, plan our menu, go online to look up nutritional information at a restaurant, and we go at it hammer and tongs. And the plan works.

Then something happens perhaps in one major thud or in niggling irritations, and we get off track. As with New Year's resolutions, we take it as a pass to abandon our efforts, and we fall back into our old patterns.

We can do that for the rest of our lives, or we can put on our big girl panties and deal with it. It's a decision to make the changes we need to make to get the result we want whatever it takes, *or* we own the fact that our choices give us the results we've had, and we'll love every corpulent inch of us. Either choice is okay when that's what you want. Just be honest with yourself.

Start with a plan that worked for you in the past. What elements helped you most? What made you feel good while shredding through the pounds? Was it the food choices? Was it an exercise plan? Did you have support or competition? Was someone holding you accountable? Or did you draw the motivation from somewhere within yourself?

If you've tried a plan several times and didn't see good results, that may not be the plan for you—or maybe it wasn't the plan for you at the time. It's okay. We all have times when our determination and motivation varies, and our bodies and emotions change a bit over time as well. Even if the "It Plan" works for every person you know but not for you, choose the one you can follow and follow cheerfully. It may work, but if it leaves you grumpy, it's not a good long-term strategy.

Yes, long-term strategy. "What we've always done" gets us the results we've always had. That's part of the dilemma with diets—once we go off the "diet" and return to giving in on too many cravings, we take in too much food and our bodies can't burn the calories. It never could. Again, nutritional plans we utilize as diets are training for longer term management.

We can have the foods we love and crave occasionally, but having those foods daily and with abandon means we'll face an incredible challenge in maintaining our weight anywhere in the vicinity of our goal. However, when we are able to enjoy those foods now and again, and truly enjoy them without feeling guilty, they somehow are more satisfying. They again become the treat and all the more special for the anticipation. By skipping the guilt, we don't end up with that need for comfort from beating up ourselves. See how that works?

It does help if you know what your body needs in terms of nutrition. Every diet guru believes that their plan is the best. It worked for them, so it's a fine enough plan as long as we follow it, as long as you can live with it happily. If your body doesn't respond well to a particular plan, it will be harder to stick to, and maintaining the loss may be a challenge. If you learn what your body needs, it's easier to find a plan that will work or hack one that almost does it for you to make it fit your needs.

In the first two months of one year I consistently and vigorously worked out, I followed the plan they suggested. I lost initially, but then it stopped. I kept working out, but I was weary all the time. They suggested more calories, and I added the prescribed number and type of foods suggested, and neither my weight nor my energy improved. I was not happy to be working out, feeling tired, and not losing anything. Go figure.

I was determined to succeed, so I did some more research looking for why I might be feeling so exhausted. In the end, a few tweaks made a difference. I adjusted my diet to fit my body's nutritional needs, and I started losing weight and gaining energy. I couldn't believe how much better I felt. Some bodies respond to more fat, others to more protein, others to more carbohydrates. Knowing your body and what works for you is essential for long-term weight management while feeling happy and energetic.

How do we do that? Whether you make mental or physical notes, for most people the answer is monitoring intake. It does require some effort to get a good sense of portion control, particular foods and how they affect us, times for meals and snacks, and all the rest of it, but there is a significant benefit to having a record of what worked and what didn't. It's easier to see areas for tweaking, how certain changes affected progress, and where we go astray if we've logged consistently. Then we can plan.

Plan for Your Food Needs

I get cranky when I'm hungry. It's my responsibility to make certain that doesn't interfere with my relationships and obligations, of course. I do my best to maintain regular meal times, and when things happen to prevent that, I'm responsible. I keep snacks in the car and my bag, an emergency stash of good-for-me options that fit within my maintenance plan and store well. If I am delayed, I have options that prevent the temptation of going into a store or restaurant in such a hungry (or "hangry") state.

Reconnaissance menu perusing is a good practice when you know a restaurant is in your future. Restaurants are filled with hidden calorie land mines. Fair play for them, food is their business, and they are trying to present appetizing and visually appealing food that the public will want again and again, which is lovely. That also presents a challenge in making good choices. Thankfully, websites often include nutritional information. I look at the online menu and plan ahead when going to a restaurant. It's easier than trying to make wise choices in the moment when I might be a little over-hungry and tempted by the choices of others, the scents wafting through the room, or the visual appeal of a dish passing by. Having two or three options in mind is helpful.

Believe

What do you know to be your best possible weight and shape? Honestly? Realistically?

Can you see yourself in that shape? At that weight? In that outfit?

If that's a challenge, then that's a place to begin. There is the odd feel-good story about the person who surprises himself by achieving something he can't imagine, but it's more consistently the person who believes it in his heart who succeeds. It's the person who is determined to follow particular self-made rules, choosing to say no to too many temptations, who stays on course. It's the person who believes it is possible to change habits who trains himself to set aside the things of the past in order to create the future desired.

They say airplanes are off course 90-something-percent of the time they fly, and pilots, auto or active, consistently return the plane to the course. My car has a habit of straying within the lane, as well, and if I don't adjust the wheels consistently, I might end up in another lane or the ditch. Yet with our food choices, we seem to leave the steering to our child-like selves rather than our wise selves. If we again take the wheel, just as we do in other areas of life, our consistent "good-for-me" choices will lead us to our goals and maintaining our weight. It will also serve us in other areas of our lives.

Will there be plateaus along the way? Probably.

Will there be temptations? Absolutely.

Will you allow yourself occasional indulgences? Emphasis on the occasional? I hope so.

We are not victims of drive-thru restaurants nor the office kitchen. We can plan around these issues, giving ourselves grace for pop-ups and then correcting our course again.

Course Corrections When It Stops Working

Stuff happens. You're cracking along, losing at whatever increment pretty steadily, and all of a sudden, it stops. Not one week but two. Call it a plateau, call it recalculating, call it a rebound even—call me frustrated.

Be gentle with yourself. It does tend to happen on every weight loss journey. The body is trying to adjust to the reduced weight. It will balance and continue. Yes, I know it's maddening in the midst. Hold on, and try any or all of these.

Hydrate. Hydrate, hydrate, hydrate. Our bodies are around 60 percent water, and it needs daily replenishing. Just do it. Even the experts disagree on whether it's plain water or whether it's flavored with coffee, tea, fruit, vegetables, or artificial flavors. Most do agree on skipping the sugar and reducing caffeine. Sugar has many harmful effects even if it does taste good, and caffeine is a diuretic, which counters our goal of hydrating. Alcohol dehydrates. Water is effective and available if you'll drink it. It helps maintain our fluid balance, which wards off retention, bloating, and all kinds of issues in the body. Dehydration can cause a headache, and no one needs that. Drink up.

Check the basics. We've all done it. We thought that was a great product, and then we realized it may have hidden sugars or some other element that clashes with our plan. The Fat-Free craze might have been okay if they hadn't replaced all the fat with sugar, creating another fat-storing trigger. They had to have something to replace the flavor of fat, and sugar was easy. Many of the energy bars, not to mention many products that aren't technically meant to be sweet, have far more sugar than we realize. We've slowly shifted our taste buds toward sweet, and in the United States, we hardly register it... apart from on our hips, of course. Or is that just me?

Read the labels, look at the ingredients, and then check the calories, carbohydrates, proteins, and fats, but also check the servings contained in the package. Sneaky devils.

My grandmother swore by two things for weight control: Fewer sugars/starches and watching overall calories. When I took my very first real job, I was a waitress, and the restaurant had an item called "The Low Cal." It consisted of a hamburger patty, cottage cheese, and lettuce or maybe it was fruit. It's been a long time. Any time my mother and I set out on a diet, it meant we were cutting out the bread, potatoes, and desserts we would serve to my brother and father. Before Low Fat or Fat Free, there was Low Starch. It worked as long as we followed it.

Then came the idea of cutting fat intake, and I actually did lose a lot of weight (and regained it again) on a low fat diet in the early 1990s. Initially, eating low fat felt like we were cheating. We could eat sugar and bread again! It didn't work for me until I watched the fat *and* calories. The issue for me was that it wasn't particularly satisfying, so I was hungry for a couple of decades as I spun up and down on my yo-yo.

Making course corrections in motion is part of the journey. Sometimes changing the foods we eat can be effective for shifting off a plateau. A client from India traveled for a month in Europe, where her food options were completely different. When she returned, she had broken through her plateau with no special diet nor exercise. Having a go-to choice makes it easy, fewer decisions and all that, but your body may need a change now and again. If you never have the same thing twice, it may be useful to find a combination you can manage and have it several days in a row. Throw your body a little bit of curve to wake it up.

Look at your food journal. And please don't throw it at me—it's not an accusation. Breathe and know that sometimes things creep in here and there for various reasons. Just have a look. If you've veered off a bit, course correct. If you've accurately logged all your food and you've stayed within your limits, YEA! Encourage yourself with your faithfulness. If you've been tinkering with a plan, logging recipes and specific foods and portions can be enlightening now and again. I've been surprised at the number of calories/carbohydrates/proteins/fats contained in a particular recipe or when I've mindlessly added a snack or haven't measured a portion for a while. We get creep, don't we? Log foods for a few days just to check in with yourself. Portion control is easy to check and it might be just the correction needed.

If you haven't kept a food journal, it can be a very useful tool. It can be as simple as keeping a notebook or a sheet of paper or as fancy as an app that breaks down every choice in terms of calories, fat, carbs, protein, sugar, fiber, and the various vitamins. Some also allow entry of weight and measurements, exercise, sleep, and vital signs, and many smart phones and/or devices also count steps and stairs. The best way to keep such a log is to choose the one you will do and do honestly. They've not yet found a way to count our calories like they can count steps we take, so we still have to enter it manually. If we do so faithfully, we can learn our patterns and see diversions. As we learn what affects us, we can plan how to increase positive effects and minimize the negative.

Consider your sleep patterns. Are you resting enough? There's a lot of research that suggests inadequate sleep makes it harder to lose weight in addition to other negative effects. It could be jacking with your metabolism and who needs that? The more tired you are, the more likely you are to give in to a snack or indulgence just because you want it and not because you are hungry or have planned for it. Our resistance to temptation is a finite resource. Add in weariness, and you could set yourself up for failure.

How many times have you started the day with a really good breakfast, skipped the doughnut offered upon arrival at the office, pivoted around the cookies in the break room, although the scent made you question your resolve. Then at lunch, everyone was having pizza, and you wanted it, you really did, but you made good-for-you food choices and went for a walk instead. At your favorite coffee place, you made a good choice, but the vendor offered you a free taste of cake, and you'd been so good. A little taste wouldn't hurt. And it should not have, but staying up late last night now has you sleepy even with a double dose of caffeine. By the time you get home, dinner goes okay, although you would have liked to have eaten the carbohydrate and fat bomb combination that stared at you from someone else's plate. You have a couple of hours of work to do, so you reason the bomb would have blown up your plans.

You manage to get through dinner and sit down for your work, and then you find your favorite snack in your desk drawer, or maybe someone innocently left it in your path. Initially you leave it, but it's staring at you while you work, even whispering your name. A call from a colleague interrupts your flow of concentration, and by the time you get off the call, an emotional tired joins the physical, and you're frustrated. The snack barely even looks your direction, and you snap it up rationalizing that you've been really good all day, and you need the release. Then you need something to drink, and the carb and fat bomb is right there in the refrigerator. Oh, why not? It's just one meal. I've been good all day.

In the morning, you awake from a "not-so-good-for-me" stupor berating yourself and wondering why you can't resist temptation after you'd done well all day. Big sigh.

Get plenty of rest. It helps us make better choices when we're not choosing from the place of "I'm tired and need comfort."

Consider your stress level. Stress eating is almost a parlor game, and we share our stress fix with others in the form of bowls on our desks as an open invitation to calm ourselves or sweeten a situation. One receptionist admitted that people who might normally storm her desk are a little kinder when they know they can score a sugary treat. It may feel like an effective comfort in the moment, but like all comfort foods, too much of a good thing is counterproductive.

Just as facing your stuff and resolving issues can foster internal rather than external comfort, resolving issues of stress deletes the need for stress-fueled eating. Of course we can't delete every stress from our lives. Stress pushes us to growth and creativity, it motivates us, and sometimes it's just a dose of reality. Often, however, it seems stress makes us feel a little helpless, at its mercy. Why?

My knees have been known to knock together when I give a presentation or speak in front of a crowd. The anticipation is no picnic either. Give me a deadline, and I'm fearful of somehow not making it even when I always do. I was the one who did homework first, then went out to play. I shocked one of my university professors by handing in a research paper a month early. I don't like the stress of a deadline staring at me when I'm trying to work and create. Many people believe they do their best work under that circumstance, but I'm not in that group, although we all used to meet at the refrigerator to soothe whatever panic we felt.

What's behind that? Fear, perhaps? Late hour unexpected obstacles or challenges might pop up and mean the project takes longer than we are given? Anxiety about performing well, perhaps? An authority

138 · RENÉE JONES

figure's response? Ultimatums that would affect our employment? Expectations of ourselves?

All are very normal issues, and food is the quick soother while we work hard at it all. How long does that soothing last? Maybe just long enough to extract your hand again from the bag of chips or to unwrap another candy, and then what? Extract the food and the issues remain, don't they? As with any comfort eating, identify the need, the possible solutions, and the exacerbating factors.

What's going on?

What do I need?

What am I saying to myself about the situation? Are my thoughts making it worse or better? How can I adjust my thinking to help me in this situation?

What are my options for soothing that will support me?

What will actually meet my need that I can get in this moment?

We do not have to be trapped in our stress responses, and yet we do tend to just go with them, don't we? It's easy to get stuck, winding ourselves up tighter and tighter when it doesn't help us. The food doesn't resolve the issue, does it? Yet we go back to it over and over. It's comfort, I get it. It's a moment's comfort amidst the storm over which we feel we have no control, and it's still like jumping out of a frying pan and into the fire. In the end, it doesn't help and likely makes our situation worse.

What will lower the stress and support your goals? Make a list of options that will feed your heart.

Evaluate your exercise. Sometimes a small boost can create a plateau buster. An extra five or 10 minutes, another thousand steps or so, an extra workout that week, a completely different form of exercise or any other movement can surprise and delight your body with something new.

Power through it. Sometimes the body just needs a moment, week, fortnight, 21 days, or whatever to readjust. Hang in there. If you indulge yourself, you'll definitely break that plateau but not likely in the way you want.

Some find that they stay at one weight for a period of time and then drop three or four pounds all at once. A plateau will break eventually. It's frustrating in the midst of it, but returning to our old choices will create what we've always had, and who would enjoy that alternative?

The Elimination Diet

Many diets have an induction phase. They eliminate all forms of certain food groups: All carbs, all dairy, all gluten, all sugars, all taste . . . oops. Did that make it to print? The idea is to eliminate certain categories that could be culprits in the case of your expanding waist line as well as "detox" us from the usual suspects for most. This can be almost painful as it messes with our chemistry; however, the variation might be just the push we need to get off a plateau. Give it a shot and see how it works for you. It sometimes provides some really helpful information. I call it playing with my food, and that just makes it more fun. I can do fun.

If you've eliminated everything and are nearly starving on a number of calories too low for your height and body type, consider adding a few calories. Some plateaus have been burst through by a cheeseburger, but no counselor from any particular national weight loss company ever told me that. Really. Nope, nope, nope.

Charles F. Glassman prescribes an elimination diet I can support: "Remove anger, regret, resentment, guilt, blame, and worry. Then watch your health, and life, improve."

I'd add shame to that list.

And it's true! Think about it. How much of our emotional baggage comes in these packages? How many of these are triggers for comfort eating? Disarm them. Chuck them out! Anger gives us lines around our mouths, regret only entangles us, resentment only keeps you angry (see previous note about lines), guilt serves no real purpose after you've acquired it, blame only passes along guilt, shame is counterproductive, and worry only adds to our stress and takes nothing away from the issue we're worried about. Strategizing? Sure. Brainstorming? Of course. Problem solving is fine—worry is a waste of energy.

I know they're hard to let go of when you've been carrying them for a long time. Believe me, I know. It takes time to choose to unpack, and yet the benefits are immediate and inexplicably lovely. Trust me on this. It's nicer in my world.

Shifting Gears

One of my clients does not like cooked vegetables, and most diets tend to heavily emphasize vegetables. We looked at what she does like and worked out ways to meet her nutritional needs, and yet the idea of staring down a green bean still left her cold. It took some time, brainstorming, and soul searching, but she came to this:

I have this thing in my head that says I don't like vegetables. One of the things I've had to do is say to myself, okay, that's not true. It's okay to make a list of vegetables that you do like, concentrate on those, and not make yourself eat the ones you don't like.

What I've discovered is that it isn't that I don't like vegetables. It's that I don't like ALL vegetables, and I don't like them prepared in all ways. That honest assessment of what I need to be eating to get healthier and then allowing myself to be choosy within what could be a broad spectrum, lets me narrow it down to what I do like.

We have that childhood admonition to "just try it." Somehow there is the notion that in order to be healthy, you have to like that whole compendium of vegetables, and in spite of your mother telling you that you might like them, you really didn't. So I try to find the ones that I do like. Much to my delight, there's a bigger list than I thought there would be.

For Your Consideration

What nutritional plan has worked for you in the past?

Are there elements of other plans that would satisfy your needs as well as help you reach your goals?

Over what have you stumbled in the past?

How can you safeguard your plan against those blocks?

Do you believe you can reach your goal?

Do you believe you can stay there?

What would it take for YOU to be able to stay at your goal weight?

Where might we need to face our child-like selves and make adult choices?

Consider Charles F. Glassman's elimination diet. "Remove anger, regret, resentment, guilt, blame, and worry. Then watch your health, and life, improve." What would your life be like if you eliminated all of these elements? Would you be willing to try?

"Food is the most abused anxiety drug. Exercise is the most underutilized antidepressant." Unknown

CHAPTER ELEVEN

Exercise

Quick Start Guide: Things That Work

Weight loss is still about nutrition. Exercise is helpful, but the formula for weight loss is 80 percent nutrition, 20 percent everything else.

I worked out three times a week for a year at a gym, one of those kickboxing sort of circuits, so I was getting a good workout. I was walking my dog five to six times a week for three and a half miles, including the days I did the workout. I worked out two to three other days per week with an online challenge that required about 10 minutes.

The weight should have been falling off me, right?

The problem was that I was a bit inconsistent with my nutrition. When I focused on it, logged my foods along with the exercise, I lost a pound each week. When I did not, my weight did not budge. Since the only difference was logging the food, I can only confess that when I wasn't writing it down, I wasn't paying as much attention. There is an accountability in knowing that if I put this in my mouth, I'm going to have to write it down—too much reality in the black and white on the page or screen.

Weight loss: 80 percent nutrition, 20 percent everything else. You can't overeat or choose the wrong foods for you and lose. You can choose so many additional calories or good-for-you foods and maintain, but you can't overindulge daily and lose. Our bodies don't work that way. Dang it.

What I most want to say about exercise is: Do some. Anything. Just move a little every day.

I lost the last 20 pounds (finally!) without a sit up, lunge, or bicep curl. I walked. That's it. And I saw lovely sunrises and sunsets. I watched grass grow and the trees change through the seasons. I saw the moon and a couple of lunar eclipses—even a blood moon. I saw rabbits, and squirrels, and birds, and one really huge out-of-place tortoise after a heavy rain.

I met a community of pre-dawn runners and other walkers. I knew the names of their dogs first but eventually learned the names of the people. I put in my ear buds and listened to music, books, learning series, and podcasts, learning a lot and stopping now and again to say hello or walk a round of the park path with someone.

I started with a short walk, and it became a sanctuary.

My weight loss quest might have been a bit faster and more shaping if I'd done more weight bearing exercise, at least more than lifting bags of mulch, rock, and compost as I did my usual gardening or the 44-pound bags of food for our dog. Toned muscles do burn more calories, and the weight bearing exercise is good for our skeletal structure.

Yet, at the time, I felt I was doing well just to get the walk in five days a week. My dawn patrol was easier to fit into the day. If I left it to later in the day, there were too many conflicts, temptations, and opportunities, and my walk got lost in the shuffle. The key was finding the exercise I would do and the time I would most likely do it consistently. Start with where you are and what you enjoy. Do you need a partner to meet you? Are you more likely to go if you have flexibility in the time? Do you need variety? Will you be more consistent with a workout video or a piece of home equipment—and you will never allow that equipment to become a hangar for laundry that needs to be ironed or put away, right? Do you prefer a sport or game, and can you organize a consistent appointment? Whatever you enjoy or can arrange, the best exercise is the one you will actually do on a regular basis.

Gym Rat and Effective Intervals

YouTube has a plethora of workout videos for every exercise choice and style, from beginner "please don't make me so sore I can't move for three days" options to hard core ripped muscle options, from a casual workout to 90-day challenges. Work out help has never been easier to access. Or if you prefer or need to go somewhere as an effective means of getting it done, sign on with a local gym or club. Download a printed workout or use a DVD. Kettlebells, machines, free weights, kickboxing, yoga, Pilates, martial arts, Tai Chi, and variations of aerobics are at your service and free.

The road is waiting when you're ready to run or walk or skip or prance at your own pace and convenience.

I see "Boot Camp" and short-term fitness groups meet in the park. It doesn't have to be a bricks and mortar operation, but it can be if that suits your needs.

Or do interval training. HIIT, which actually doesn't stand for Hyped Infinitum Interval Training but High Intensity Interval Training, took the yo-yo community by storm as the solution to burning calories faster and more effectively. How long did you stay with your new training regime? Did you download an interval timer to tell you when to pump it up? Did you respond to that Ahooga horn with more than a groan?

We are so easy—"magic weight loss" process announced, and we're there sleeping at the end of the string again.

Does it work? Sure. When you do it. Intense short bursts of 100 percent effort with active recovery bursts raises your heart rate, builds muscle, and burns calories. Helps me if someone is around to push me to that kind of effort when I slack off or grow weary. Perhaps you're better at keeping at it than I am. Those who can find their groove and stay in it consistently will see results.

A good workout takes a short time, maybe 10 to 30 minutes, and you're done. I spent a year with one gym because a trainer type was patrolling the workout area shouting encouragement or correction to form, it only took 30 minutes three times a week, and I was done. Couldn't argue with that, and the staff kept us focused if we wanted to be. Couldn't skip it—it was only 30 minutes! I could find 30 minutes. Then I got a bit bored with the routine, so I signed on for a 90-day challenge with an online workout that only took 10 minutes. I was consistent for the 90 days. It was hard to ignore as it only required 10 minutes, and I didn't have to leave the house. Sometimes we need a bit of change, and over time we can collect options that keep us entertained, challenged, and toned.

Exercise works to build or tone muscle which burns more calories. It's good for us. Exercise makes us breathe more and more deeply, it's good for our bones, and it helps maintains some flexibility.

And yet, many of us don't find a way to incorporate it. We don't have the time, we don't want to sweat and clean up, we don't enjoy the activity, it makes me sore, I don't want to get bulky, and any other reason on your mind. The good news is that it will help, but it's not the key to losing pounds. Again, the key is nutrition. If you work out and don't lose a pound or an inch, look at nutrition. It's too easy to think that if we work out, we can add back in the chocolate cake we're craving. We burned the calories, right? Sure, we can do that if we're trying to maintain our weight, but to lose, we have to manage our food intake. Weight loss is 80 percent nutrition... okay, I know, you've got that by now. I find it annoying, too. It doesn't seem fair, does it? Maybe if we add that supplement... and yes, you've got that concept as well by now.

The only way I manage to keep myself working out consistently is to work with my individual preferences. I don't want big muscles. I'm not a sleeveless kind of girl, so having my guns cut and defined doesn't motivate me. As a pear shape, I'm much more concerned with my waist, hips, and legs, and I don't want any of that part of my body to enlarge. Toned, yes, enlarged no. When I do weight bearing exercises, I focus there, and I find other ways to make it fit me, fit my needs and desires, fit my schedule and lifestyle. Find what works for you, your schedule, goals, desires, needs, and lifestyle—and make it fun.

Common/Easy Additions to Make It Fun

The best exercise for us is the exercise we will do consistently. So, what do you do as a hobby, as part of your home life, as part of your social life? You've seen the lists of ways to burn a few extra calories here and there like parking farther away or taking the stairs rather than an elevator. Sometimes when we see such things so often, we immediately dismiss them without consideration. "Oh yeah, that again. Tried that, and I didn't see any difference."

Did you try it with nutrition in check? Weight management is a combination of factors, and perhaps there was another widget out of place. Are there any of those options we can choose to make our habit? Or are there any tasks we've outsourced that we can take back and use as exercise? Reconsider these common options for incidental exercise.

Mow your own lawn or clean your own house or parts of your house. If you have outsourced it, maybe cut your service back to every other week, and you do the one in between. It will save you some cash and give you some exercise while accomplishing a task.

Plant a flower or vegetable garden. Even a small one requires some digging and then tending as it grows through the seasons. Planter gardens still require us to lug home bags of potting soil, compost, and mulch.

Play tag with your kids or dog. Play anything with your kids or dog. Get outside and interact—it will do you as well as them a lot of good. Breathe a little fresh air.

Walk through one of the big box stores—they're usually good for almost a mile if you go from one side to the other and back while shopping. I may be guilty of motivating myself to shop, which isn't one of my favorite activities, to get the added steps. Big hardware stores are really good for a game of hide and seek with your friends or the kids. Hey, I said make it fun. Did you not believe me?

Take an extra lap around the mall or shopping center instead of making it a quick mission of acquisition and exit. Park at the opposite end of your intended target, and enjoy the stroll.

Ankle weights or a weighted vest can be subtle if you want it to be. One really annoying fact is that carrying extra weight does burn more calories whether it's body weight or ankle weights, so I burned more when I weighed more. To balance that out a bit, I added ankle weights now and again just to surprise my metabolism.

Drink more water. It's just good for you, and it will require more steps to and from both the kitchen and the bathroom.

Walk instead of drive when it's practical.

Release your inner pacer. In school they made us sit still as part of learning discipline, crowd control, and focus. Guess what? You're no longer in school. Walk or pace as you think or talk on the phone. It's okay. It relieves stress, adds steps, and invests energy in whatever you're doing.

Consider getting a treadmill desk or one that allows you to stand, or if you prefer sitting, try a stability ball instead of a chair. The movement is incidental but it adds up.

Practice breathing deeply. The pace of life often has us breathing rapid, shallow breaths. Take two minutes and breathe deep connected breaths. It will relax you and give your lungs the workout they really need for optimum function.

Give yourself a few playful rules that will amuse you:

Always take the stairs for three floors or fewer.

If I have to wait more than 10 seconds for the elevator to arrive, I take the stairs at least three floors.

When I visit X Big Box store, I always park no closer than Y, and I walk from A department to Z department just because I want to.

I set a timer on my phone for every hour (or two), and I stop whatever I'm doing and breathe for two minutes. Or I make a quick dash up and down the hallway every X number of hours/minutes.

I use a pedometer to keep account and get 10,000 (or 15,000 or 20,000) steps, X number of days per week.

If my pedometer reaches X number of steps, I always take a quick walk to round the number up to Y.

I carry groceries from the car to the house one bag at a time. Even if it's just from the garage 10 feet from the kitchen, those steps add up. Endless options ensue. Perhaps carry items to the other parts of the house in certain numbers like only two per trip to the bathroom or one per trip upstairs.

The point is that it doesn't matter if you sweat out your water bottle twice over or work your way up to a marathon. The point is to move. Just some. Breathe some fresh air. It's a great stress buster, and it helps burn calories.

Plan a Habit

Habits make their ways into our lives for good and ill. We know it can take persistence to break those we no longer want, and creating habits we do want can be just as fragile. Tenacity pays off and lends its own brand of encouragement.

In Gretchen Rubin's book, *Better Than Before*, she identifies individual tendencies and traits that support habit formation and supplies strategies that work for extracting, instilling, and/or supporting those habits. My type, an "obliger," is very good at helping others hold to their habits and goals, but I need accountability to someone to meet my own. It's as natural as being a redhead, blond, brunette, or raven, so I just go with it.

After reading *Better Than Before*, knowing my "obliger" tendency and my distinctive traits, I set off with one of Rubin's strategies to limit my sugar intake to Sundays only, as noted earlier. Although sugar had historically been a daily habit and sought as if it were an essential nutrient for me, and I feared it would be hard and I would feel deprived, I was determined to reduce my excessive sugar use. Seemed like an adult decision with all the attendant health benefits. I didn't even wait until Monday to start as I have for so many other changes; I just zipped straight into it and asked someone to hold me accountable. Please step away from the pantry and refrigerator!

Habits take time, and I found myself more than once staring down chocolate chips, ice cream, or whatever happened to be nearby. To bolster my resolve, I repeated, "I only have sugar on Sundays." Sooner than I anticipated, the feeling in my words shifted from, "I committed myself, told someone about it, and now I have to do it, so please step away from the sugar," to, "I choose to have sugar only on Sundays," to "What am I doing in here? I only want sugar on Sundays," to not even thinking of having sugar during the week. The change in the feelings around it morphed from feeling a little sad to feeling encouraged to feeling empowered. I had control around sugar again.

It took just over a week, and I didn't even think to break my rule for two months when my husband's birthday came up in the middle of the week.

Oh, now we've been down this road before. I have resolved to make consistent choices, eliminate food groups, never have X again in my quest to lose X number of pounds. It went well as long as I didn't deviate. Once I deviated, I was sleeping at the end of the yo-yo string again. Insidious.

"Hey, you have a habit to support your intentions. Use it," I screamed at myself. To bolster my intentions and meet my needs, I enlisted my husband's help. We had a lovely day, he had a wonderful coconut, almond, dark chocolate mousse cake, and I planned around the indulgence. Then I jumped right back into my habit that I continue to practice. On the odd occasion, I may have one square of really dark chocolate, the 77 percent variety, and I allow that indulgence before returning to my habit. Having that kind of flexibility and control strengthens the mental structure behind the habit for me. It may not work that way for everyone as some have more control of themselves and some can bear no temptation or deviation from the rule, so choose the structures that will work for you. Play with your options until you find the combination that helps you.

Installing a habit of walking was easy given the dog's rehab schedule, and with the second round, I decided we would just keep going. My dog was more than game, and the exercise improved his behavior as well. Adding a gym workout took some effort, and yet the common thread was the motivator—someone or something was expecting me, which is a significant and effective motivator for me. Not everyone needs that or finds it helpful, but it worked for me.

Analyze how you work best, what motivates you to do a new task. Piece together the parts of the puzzle that will encourage you to continue. Habits both good and bad are created both consciously and unconsciously, and we can find the ones that support our goals.

Exercise: All Kinds

So perhaps physical exercise isn't so appealing. Again, weight loss is 80 percent nutrition, so you can lose weight without it, and I'd still encourage you to try a little once in a while. Even sitting outside and breathing in fresh air will be beneficial. If you want to wander around a little while you're out there, maybe look at some flowers or trees, that could be rejuvenating.

There are other things we can exercise: Caution, control, wisdom, grace, kindness, rest, habit change, prudence, self-control, solitude, interaction, skills, talents, your heart, your mind, challenges, beliefs, sharing your abundance. Almost makes a five-minute walk sound easy, doesn't it?

In math, two plus two equals four. So does one plus three, zero plus four, and nine minus five. I'm sure my math genius friends have plenty of other ways to get to four. All are right, all will get to four. It may not be your preferred way, but that's kind of beside the point. Exercise your options, and a few questions for reflection could be:

How could you exercise kindness both in a traditional and unconventional sense?

When might you find a time, place, or opportunity to rest physically, emotionally, or mentally that would also challenge yourself as well as show grace to another?

How might you arrange a walk or some kind of exercise and share time with someone else?

Play with the elements and see what creative and fulfilling options might emerge. In the end, exercise doesn't have to be drudgery. It was meant to be fun, so take the opportunity to play.

Shifting Gears

One client has a number of allergies, so food choices are fairly limited. She gets a fair amount of exercise in her work, and yet getting in exercise that supports her weight management goals is a little harder. She found focusing on the small things helped to get in some exercise and some significant stress reduction.

"Take a five-minute walk. Take five minutes to breathe. Do small things every day. I wasn't overwhelmed, and by starting small, I could build time doing the things I like."

It's a good idea. We often create grand goals. Grand goals are supported by many small pieces and a determination to get there. What is the smallest step you could take to creating a new exercise option to help you meet your goal?

For Your Consideration

What forms of exercise have you enjoyed?

What stopped you from continuing exercise in the past?

How might you reconnect with previous exercise options?

We all have pieces of exercise equipment scattered around, some we used consistently for a period of time. How can you utilize them now to help you meet your goal?

What exercise could you incorporate into your day consistently?

At what time of day would you most likely be able to exercise consistently? Days of the week?

Do you need someone to hold you accountable? Or is there another way you can maintain consistency?

What are a few habits or fun rules you could make for yourself to have a little fun with exercise?

Do you need a variety of exercise options each week?

"All happenings, great and small, are parables whereby God speaks. The art of life is to get the message." Malcolm Muggeridge

CHAPTER TWELVE

A Word from the Chaplain

Quick Start Guide: Things That Work

Running through life, keeping our issues at bay with a doughnut, seeking relief from the drive-thru menu does not heal our hearts. A colleague summed up the crux of the issue:

"A two-second attention span." I wish that phrase was only used in reference to the children that reside in my home. Yet I have learned that phrase applies to me at my worst.

I run through life and forget to pay attention, and that's when I snack, eat because I'm stressed, depressed, or any other excuse of which I might think.

Sometimes, something around me reminds me to stop and pay attention—pay enough attention to ask myself, "Am I hungry or just eating?"

What is it my body really wants? If it really wants food, what good food can I give this machine that keeps me running, that will help it keep running? The questions and answers vary based on the situation.

Too many times I forget to pay attention to life. When I actually do put 100 percent into where I am, who I am with, and what I am doing, my need for food diminishes. The challenge before me is always to pay attention.

Pay attention. Your heart is worth it.

"Authenticity to one's self is the only thing you can own. I urge you to fight for it, and if it's gonna be a war, finish the battle yourself." I do not know where that statement came from. It may have been a quote from a book or a podcast. I found it scribbled on a piece of paper in my stack, and I find it compelling.

We spend countless hours with others who want us to conform to their views of the world and of us. Shakespeare said it through Polonius in Hamlet, "To thine own self be true." Granted, a lot has been made of this quote that differs from the original meaning, and I'm about to add to that with this: We are not often as true to ourselves as we could or would like to be. We conform, we contort, we wear masks, and we often lose a sense of who we truly are, and that creates issues. We please our parents and pursue a degree or occupation they chose. We stop doing things we love to please our partner who really can't stand that activity. We shape our habits and choices to please others—and we slowly lose our sense of self.

So we eat to make up for the sense of loss, the discomfort, the residual negative feelings. Food is an area where we can claim a dose of comfort. We can choose the foods that bring us the most pleasure or even just one moment now and again that transcends the ordinary or the painful. We'd choose food we know, love, and can count on to relieve the many moments with which we are unfamiliar or afraid, to soothe the feelings from results we didn't expect, or to just control some moment of ecstasy. Some do drugs, alcohol, and/or sex, but food is easy to access, legal, acceptable, and plentiful in Western culture.

Then we gain enough weight to displease others as well as ourselves. Isn't it interesting that we are less likely to successfully conform when someone criticizes our weight? No, the criticism gives us another reason to eat to soothe ourselves. In fact, the criticism may drive us toward an all-you-can-eat buffet even faster. At some point, we give up trying to please others in this area, and we don't want to give up our comfort foods even if our bodies are screaming for relief.

It's not about a diet or exercise, it's a need for healing.

Ever had a toothache? Miserable experience, and like many infections, it makes your whole body hurt. When we hurt, we tend to focus on only the hurt—what we're losing with it—and our view gets very narrow. Painkillers may help, and distraction is a good thing as it directs our focus anywhere but on the pain. What we most need, however, is healing through a dentist or medication.

Whether it's an infection physically or emotionally, old wounds seldom heal spontaneously. It needs an antibiotic or extraction, clean bandages, and time for the healing to occur. Ignoring the pain doesn't heal it. Further destructive behavior makes it worse. We focus on managing our pain, but what we need is to heal the source of the pain.

Our "stuff" will not go away on its own. We self-medicate when it needs attention and the pain subsides for the moment, but it roars back the next time we're stressed, tired, or upset. It needs healing. When we face our stuff and truly sort it out, the pain dissipates, and it doesn't return in the same way. Everything improves. Birds sing, the grass is green, little things don't bother us—why would we need comfort foods? There may still be issues along the way, but we grow stronger, and we're more capable of handling stressors. We learn what we need to do for ourselves, and that makes us less susceptible to fads, magic potions, and crazy remedies. We'll already have the remedy—and we actually had it all along if we had been able to recognize it. Our hearts will be healed, and we'll have no limp, and we will not need the crutches we use as coping mechanisms.

A very skilled and patient colleague walked through the bulk of my story with me. I was finally fed up with the yo-yo, with struggling with my inversely conjoined weight and self-esteem, one so dependent on the other that they fed off and consumed each other. That needed separation. I'd functioned with my coping mechanisms for so long that I no longer recognized the ties that bound me to my wounds nor that my perspective could be a teensy weensy bit skewed.

She challenged my assumptions, questioned the basis of beliefs, and played devil's advocate with my choices, actions, and self-righteous justifications. Abundant patience gave me space and support as I worked to reconfigure and unpack more baggage than either of us bargained for. It was a bumpy ride, a circuitous route at times as she sometimes challenged me to frustration. Her intentions were for my good, and eventually my heart healed, and that set me free.

She still challenges me now and again, and I welcome it because she calls me to my best, and I want that. Yep, I want to be my best self more than chocolate, more than peanut butter, more than any favored coping mechanism, and that was and still is a surprise.

When we no longer need the crutches we've used to cope, we lose our attachment to them. They are no longer a temptation. Our priorities naturally fall into place, and we are generally happier. When our hearts heal, it makes the world seem different, an amazing and abundant place. Rather than seeing the dangers and the flaws in others, we see possibilities and good intentions.

As a reformed cynic, it still amazes me to think this way. I couldn't even have conceived of it a few short years ago. I would have said that's being naïve or silly. There are real dangers out there, and they might affect me. It's better to be on one's guard, be not only aware but watchful for potential pitfalls or disaster, get out before you get hurt, and all the rest of it. Yet it doesn't help me to focus on them unless they actually do affect me. Perhaps they never will, and then I would have wasted an awful lot of energy worrying about the negative possibilities. Going out of our way to avoid dangers can rob us of opportunities.

When my mother was ill, it was quite a shock. She had been quite healthy all of her life until she wasn't. She had a brain tumor. As a hospital chaplain, I was familiar with the routine and the possibilities. I'd watched families walk through this and other issues. In a fit of wisdom, I realized I could worry myself sick and be exhausted, or I could wait to see what was actually going on before I leapt into that abyss of worry. If I needed the energy to cope with a terminal diagnosis, I would have it. If it turned out to be treatable, I would save myself from the physical and emotional exhaustion such worry creates.

I see the potential dangers of life certainly, and yet I prefer to conserve energy rather than waste it. I also prefer to look for what's going well, where blessings may pop up, what's good in others over being so prepared to counter potential issues. And that's a marvelous perspective from which to do life. Having been through a similar cynical stage, my colleague offered what had been offered to her: "All you believe may be true and justified, but it's nicer in my world."

It is, indeed.

I know the struggle of the yo-yo dieter. I know the thinking that food will soothe us through this issue. I know there are challenges all along the way. I also know it's worth denying that tendency, finding another way to soothe that both works more effectively and feels better the moments and hours afterward.

Yet I'm less concerned about the numbers—gain a few, lose a few, and the loss will outstretch the gain in time. That's just surface stuff, and it belies what's underneath, and that untouched stuff underneath still drives the comfort eating. What I'm most concerned with is transformation. Instead of building an alibi for whatever weakness I'm trying to cover up, I want to build strength to overcome my weaknesses. I want healing. We can resolve and finish with this issue.

It's possible to shift our feelings and thinking so that we no longer use food as a pacifier. At that point, we no longer need a "diet."

Face your stuff, and you will no longer have to stuff your face.

Imagine that.

What would it be like? What would you see, taste, smell, touch, hear? What would you wear? What would you do? How would it feel?

What you can imagine, you can become because it's already part of you. It may be buried, but it hasn't gone anywhere. It can be excavated.

Close your eyes and imagine the best version of you. Physically, emotionally, in your spirit, in your career, in your family. Deck that vision out with the best of yourself, your best intentions, your quiet thoughts and aspirations, what you would dream to be true.

Here's the kicker—it is already true. That best vision of yourself may not be fully realized yet, may be buried under life experiences, but it's true—once we extract all the masks we've used to protect ourselves, the coping mechanisms, and the limps in our souls. That best vision is who you are, who you were made to be, who you can be if you have eyes to see and ears to hear.

Let go of any part of you that doesn't believe it. How does holding onto the vision of your lesser self-help you? You're the only one holding you to it, and why would you want to do that? Extract the masks, the coping mechanisms, the way you compensate for the wounds in your heart. Let them go. Fly, be free.

If you believed that's who you truly were, how would you be different?

The truest you will emerge when you give it the space and encouragement to emerge. It may take a little time and some practice, play, and experimenting, but it's you, so it's there for the finding. If you don't wish to do this archaeological dig by yourself, find a qualified coach, counselor, or friend to help you. You're worth excavating.

St. Catherine of Siena said, "Be who God meant you to be, and you will set the world on fire."

Go forth and conquer.
So let it be written, so let it be done.

"Forgive yourself for not knowing what you didn't know before you learned it." – *Zig Ziglar*

CPSIA information can be obtained
at www.ICGtesting.com
Printed in the USA
BVOW03*0128010917
493741BV00008B/50/P